# JABBERWOCKY

# JABBERWOCKY

*ut modo defuncti tepidique cadaueris ora
plena uoce sonent . . .*

since the mouth of a body newly dead and still warm
speaks in a richer voice . . .
—Lucan, *Civil War.*

**PRIME BOOKS**

# TABLE OF. . .

The Second Coming, *William Butler Yeats* . . . . . . . . . . . . . . 7

The Psychic Above Burritoville, *Mike Allen* . . . . . . . . . . . . . 9

Sir Walter Raleigh in Guiana, *Veronica Schanoes* . . . . . . . . 15

The Music of the Dead, *Jennifer Crow* . . . . . . . . . . . . . . . . 30

The Dark Lady, *Megan Messinger* . . . . . . . . . . . . . . . . . . . 32

Whitechapel Autumn, 1888, *Ann K. Schwader* . . . . . . . . . 50

Suttee, *Catherynne M. Valente* . . . . . . . . . . . . . . . . . . . . . 51

Diminishing, *Tim Pratt* . . . . . . . . . . . . . . . . . . . . . . . . . . 57

The Tongueless Bell, *Constance Cooper* . . . . . . . . . . . . . . 59

Fix, *Jeannelle M. Ferreirra* . . . . . . . . . . . . . . . . . . . . . . . 61

Countries of the Sun, *Sonya Taaffe* . . . . . . . . . . . . . . . . . . 66

Escape, *Rio Le Moignan* . . . . . . . . . . . . . . . . . . . . . . . . . . 71

Medea, *Sarah Koplik* . . . . . . . . . . . . . . . . . . . . . . . . . . . . 72

Miranda, *JoSelle Vanderhooft* . . . . . . . . . . . . . . . . . . . . . 74

# . . .CONTENTS

The Shape of Mistake, *Laurel Winter* . . . . . . . . . . . . . . . . . 77

canvas, mirror, glass, *Holly Phillips* . . . . . . . . . . . . . . . . . 82

the string, *Ainsley Dicks* . . . . . . . . . . . . . . . . . . . . . . . 110

The Relationship Between Lovers & Words, *Jaida Jones* . . 112

Ouroboros Time, *Yoon Ha Lee* . . . . . . . . . . . . . . . . . . . 119

Brillig, *Richard Parks* . . . . . . . . . . . . . . . . . . . . . . . . . 120

Arachne, *Theodora Goss* . . . . . . . . . . . . . . . . . . . . . . . 126

Beauty Sleep, *Helena Bell* . . . . . . . . . . . . . . . . . . . . . . 128

Beans, *Jane Yolen* . . . . . . . . . . . . . . . . . . . . . . . . . . . . 130

The Trickster In My Belly, *Erzebet YellowBoy* . . . . . . . . . 131

Arbor Low, *Elizabeth E. Wein* . . . . . . . . . . . . . . . . . . . . 137

New Year's Eve at West Kennet, *Sarah Singleton* . . . . . . . 138

Love Story, *Cassandra Phillips-Sears* . . . . . . . . . . . . . . . 140

Grey December, *Shirl Sazynski* . . . . . . . . . . . . . . . . . . . 146

# THE SECOND COMING
## WILLIAM BUTLER YEATS

Turning and turning in the widening gyre
The falcon cannot hear the falconer;
Things fall apart; the centre cannot hold;
Mere anarchy is loosed upon the world,
The blood-dimmed tide is loosed, and everywhere
The ceremony of innocence is drowned;
The best lack all convictions, while the worst
Are full of passionate intensity.

Surely some revelation is at hand;
Surely the Second Coming is at hand.
The Second Coming! Hardly are those words out
When a vast image out of Spiritus Mundi
Troubles my sight: somewhere in sands of the desert
A shape with lion body and the head of a man,
A gaze blank and pitiless as the sun,
Is moving its slow thighs, while all about it
Reel shadows of the indignant desert birds.
The darkness drops again; but now I know
That twenty centuries of stony sleep

Were vexed to nightmare by a rocking cradle,
And what rough beast, its hour come round at last,
Slouches towards Bethlehem to be born?

# THE PSYCHIC ABOVE BURRITOVILLE
## MIKE ALLEN

*I. introducción*

*The smell*, she says, her good eye
a candle-flame flicker in a limestone cave—
the other, blue and filmy as polluted water.
*Si, the smell, it's maddeningly good,*
*always makes my mouth water.*
Her smile, full of stalagmites.

From her ceiling, wide flat masks
hang like a legion of bats,
rock softly in no breeze,
feathers dangling from their
overburdened earlobes. Her table
is stone, a carved jaguar. Its purr
rumbles deep. Through incense haze
you glimpse withered heads,
peering from her shelves through wooden disks,
and wonder, are they real or wax—
why else would they sweat so?

And infused in the heady brew,
odors of burrito and quesadilla and flan,
arroz pollo, chili con carne, and
others you can't name—*paella,*
*pulpo, chorizo, cabra del diablo,*
she rattles, finishing your list aloud.
*My sister, she's the cook. ¿Comprende?*
The card springs like a knife from
gouty fingers. *Here she is, always*
*under your nose.* Above illuminated script,
THE COOK, indeed she's there,
plump, aproned, brown as earth.
She bustles among infinitely receding
rows of stoves, millions of dishes
bubbling and boiling and broiling,
each one a loving recombination, a new birth,
something more than the parts that went in.
*Much like you, chico, or me,* she says,
smiling stalagmites. *Let's see*
*what's cooking now.*


*ii. cartas del tarot*


I warn you, *señor*, my cards are mean,
crueller than any European's, *despiadadas!*

They are creatures of Manhattan now,
but they do not forget their roots.

So who are you, *mi polluelo?*
My fingers find THE CONQUERED MAN,
bare-backed, bloodied Indian bowed
before the Spaniard's gun. We will see,
before we're done, THE CONQUISTADOR.
Will this pitiful beast ever break his ropes,
or even stand? His party, long out of favor,
see how he shrinks within THE FACTORY,
where he labors for mere pennies a year.

Why does THE DICTATOR frown,
when his medals of power glint and his club
stands taller than mountains?
*¡O, qué cono!*—THE KNIFE FIGHT.
Who knew your heart housed such a rebel,
Conquered One? Not you. But which
is Cutter and Cut?
In the dark, their faces can't be seen.

THE DANCING GIRL twirls her red skirt
in your past, but it's her legs you were watching, mmm?
You haven't stopped spinning, and just ahead, THE CENOTE.
But where is THE VIRGIN? A beautiful chilling swim,

so many bones beneath.
What price to gain what you'll learn here?
Fear death by water.
Or perhaps just my fee.


THE GUITAR PLAYER lies with THE WIDOWED MOTHER.
He's worse than THE DANCING GIRL.
See how he changes her grief to coins?
Her children
climb her dress like hungry ants.
*¿Qué sucedío con su marido?*
Will I see her husband's face
if I draw THE DISAPPEARED?
Is he someone you betrayed? What weight
a friend's life against a sure path?


And here, what you chose to chase,
THE HEADDRESS, with plumes and dangling charms
and bulging eyes, beaten gold snarl.
Does anyone believe it? Not this man, *señor.*
Here, at last, THE CONQUISTADOR,
surrounded by *carne de cadáver,*
yet how clean his blade.
Dangerous to fight him with only
a ceremonial knife. To THE TEMPLE for aid—
pray to all the gods who might care, as you must,

but who
is there left to sacrifice?

Here is how it all turns out . . . .
*¡Cagate en Dios!* So sorry, I know
how this new smell spoils everything.
Your face, such a frightened mask—
*rápidamente*, I'll hide it away,
but you must look and remember:

these awkward mounds, gaping
mouths, staring eyes. *Si, señor*,
I too hear the flies.
THE MASS GRAVE.
There is no need, no need, no need,
for such alarm—some come here
sooner than they wish. *¿Tan qué?*
Given time, we all go.
Isn't it so sad
true cities of the dead
are so unglamourous?

*iii. el altar de piedra*

The questions clamor: where
have the succulent kitchen smells gone?

And also: *¿Dónde estás?*
Moist green oven, the jungle
grows about you like smoke,
golden fruit like shimmering masks
dangle from the vines, tempting, taunting,
protruding pulpy tongues.
*Bite us, chico, we'll bite back.*
The caverns above are filled with candle flames.
Heavy treads lumber from the mountain slopes,
hungry jaguar, voice the rumble of granite,
mouth wide as a man's shoulders,
eyes scooped from stone. Other eyes,
wooden, withered hordes, regard you
from between the leaves, victims of
THE DICTATOR'S iron club, or carved claws.
Blood in the runnels. Blood
between stalagmite teeth.

*Run, chico, run!* Her grasp is crueller
than any European's. Where
is your sacrifice? Her price
has yet to be paid.

# SIR WALTER RALEGH IN GUIANA
## VERONICA SCHANOES

### 1.

Of the like which any man can read in
Pliny and Herodotus are there amazons and tribes of headless
giants
which I have not seen.
I am told a word from me but a few days past
would have settled the matter
and I might have brought one of these
prodigies to present at court.
No matter now.

A few days ago is lost,
Yesterday has vanished as well and I am sure
there can be no hell worse than this murky, moist,
contagious air which squats on a man's chest
like a sodden monkey.
Day is as night for all we can see of the sun.
The grasping, dripping trees, warm and palpating lean in
as we beat the viscous river in a dull and nauseous panic.

The trees stretch over, pulsing,
reaching to caress our aching muscles
and absorb our starving, sweating bodies into the silt.

2.

We designed to hang the pilot.

We had taken an old Indian from a village
some weeks back for ransom of food
and information on the Spanish,
and getting the bounty, we held him still as our guide.
And now, beaten and sodden by the very air,
yellow with pus and the lying promise of gold,

We designed to hang the pilot.

And to leave his body swaying from a tree,
yet another piece of damp decaying rot in this infested place.
To use his corpse as a maggot-ridden marker of the river path
we took
because I know we've been going in deeper and deeper circles,
further mired in this place,
and dear God, we are so hungry,
and have been rowing for so long,
in this most poisonous river.

Ten hours today, at least,
and our last meal
as far away as the amazons and the headless men,
As that wrinkled old Indian squatted at the front of the boat
and told us it was just a little farther on,
just three more reaches,
for hours now.

So we designed to hang the pilot.

But, as our own concerns argued sufficient in his favor
—dear God, can *you* lead us out of this swamp—
and the pilot argued not at all,
but only sat,
like an implacable leather-eyed will-o-wisp
fading against the brown morass of mud and tree and serpent
surrounding us
fading into the bones of our boat;

As our concerns for home argued sufficient in his favor—
concerns for home free from this poisonous mist
and infectious heavy heat,
for home and court as treacherous as these bloody rivers;

As, I say, our own concerns argued sufficient in his favor,
We held off and pressed on.

3.

The serpents surround us.
The Spanish call them *lagartos*.
They are perhaps ten feet long,
perhaps longer, with large, toothy maws.
They teem and seethe beneath the surface
we stroke helplessly—
Even where the waters are clear
They are there lurking—
*They are the river bed*,
the sand beneath our hull, beneath the noisome waters
like the glittering words at court.
Their lithesome bodies twist ands stretch and ache towards us.

Towards my Will.
He could not contain himself at the sight of this country,
and it is the most beautiful that ever mine eyes beheld.
The sun rose after that night,
That night which threatened to smother us with muggy oppres-
sion.
We shrank, holding each other against the decay of the trees
which narrowed the river and reached in for us
Trailing rotting fingers over our faces, our necks,
their stench and liquid running into every pore and orifice.

We had to hack our way down the river with swords
and toss the arborial effluvia overboard.

And then the sun came up,
and we wondered at that most beautiful country,
vegetation tamed by nature for use
and crystal-clear waters.
My Will was the first of the men up,
stripping off his clothes—
all our clothing is washed ten times a day on our backs,
'til cloth begins to fuse with sodden skin,
and we've had no change of these rags for thirty days
—and he leapt into the waters.

Over the water his dark body hung for infinite minutes
as I whispered to each musky inch I longed to save,
and then he plunged into the river
(I have never heard of such another country for rivers.).
He sputtered with relief and then
The Lagartos had him.

4.

On still further rivers deep in that beautiful country
And there is water everywhere
but in our mouths our throats our lips

split and bleed, drawing the flies.
We filled our skins with river water the day before—
God if river-water were gold, this beyond doubt were Manoa
—and drank our fill
giving momentary salve to parched and cracked innards
hidden beneath sodden skin liquefying into mist.

Momentary salve for
we were doubled over all night puking up worms,
red and noisome and teeming as they poured forth.
So we've had no river-water since—no water at all
but the sweat which oozes from our skin and seeps into our
mouths.

And then I saw some young Indians,
men of the O_____ nation,
walking along the river lifting clay vessels to their lips and swallowing
easily, daintily, with restraint.
I hailed them, landed to meet them,
and almost fell to my knees
gesturing at the water.
The young men looked at each other and seemed to shrug,
and allowed me my fill,
watched me guzzle it down in shameful ecstasy.

Where?
I asked them.
Where?

One of the youths—both most comely—
spoke slowly and kindly,
as we do in the presence of the simple-minded,
and showed me the river.

And the worms?
Ah, he said, and showed me the sun.
For we must be careful to watch the sun.
In the morning, he said, the water is clear
and pure and knowable.
But in the afternoon, the river seethes.

5.

The river seethes,
explained Topiawari,
and brings forth the worms in the heat.
And it was not like that in the valley of his fathers.

The old man, 110, and being a cassique,
or great commander, of his people,
waved a straight arm

at the lands cradling us.
This, he said, was but a nook of the rolling vasty lands
claimed by his people,
before the Ewapanoma, who have their heads in their chests
and the strength of Hannibal's elephants
seized his birthright.

The old man stared at me with a sharp sorrow
and told of the battle he led
—when I was your age, Englishman—
to regain the lands of his birth
and instead lost his eldest son.
The young man was slain in battle,
never entering the winter of his life
in harmony with his aged father.

And the old man sighed with great inward feeling
for the loss of country and son,
antecedents and successor.
He set in my care his only remaining son
to accompany us to England.
I left with him
one Frauncis Sparrow, a lad who chattered all day,
in the hopes that this would help him to acquire the language
more easily

and because he was eager to tarry
and besides could describe a country well with his pen.

We drank, then, to celebrate this exchange,
to his leaving son, and his son slain,
and to my son, and to Young Sparry,
and I drank to Will, and to Elizabeth.
I asked the old man if he himself were not desirous of seeing a
far-away land
(for so England is to him)
and the Great Virgin Cassique,
Ezrabeta Cassipuna Aquerewana, her majesty
(and that is as much as saying Elizabeth, the great princesse,
or greatest commander)
but Topiawari Cassique
avowed that he was old and weak,
and was every day called for by death,
which was his own phrase.

And so he turned towards home.
And so we pressed on to Manoa.

6.

Topiawari would not reveal to us
the secret of the poison arrows

which can kill a man by only grazing his flesh.
Having been touched by one,
the unfortunate runs away, considering himself safe
and is then brought to his knees retching dark bile
and cannot be calmed.
He passes in and out of delirium
clawing for breath
clawing at his stomach until the blood runs through his fingers
and finally he dies. His innards, black with rot,
burst through his skin and crawl out his mouth.

Though not one man of mine has fallen victim.
Not one.

And the course of this poison is unstoppable
by any known means.
And I know not whence it is derived.
And I know no cure
*But one exists—*
For the tribesmen of these forests all carry an antidote,
One swig of which overcomes the poison.
Topiawari would not reveal it.

But, as I say,
not one of my men has needed it.

For these are an amicable and accommodating people,
bearing boundless love for us
because of our forbearance.
We seize nothing of theirs,
take nothing by stealth or by force—
(though it is near impossible to control the baser men.
When I hear of some offense
I publicly chastise the man and offer reparations)
*And we do not touch their women.*

This is why we are so beloved.
The Spaniards, they tell us,
take wives and daughters,
maidens and matrons at whim.
And though their women greet us,
naked and comely and not, I think, unwilling,
we do not touch them.

There was one woman,
one lady, not like the others.
She was a lady of steady maturity
who held herself with such calm possession
that all the village became as background to her.
And as much as she excelled and led the other tribeswomen of
the town,
So too did she command the respect of men.

She sat among them
smoking and drinking,
discussing the past and future.

(Her black hair fell in coarse curls
and plaits down her back.
Her heavy dark brows leapt and creased as she talked—
*I spoke not one immodest word to her. I swear.*
She was heavy about the hips and arms
and brooked no insolence;
I did see her carelessly strike down a young man,
perhaps her nephew.)

She was gracious, powerful in bearing,
and but for the coloring, she was a near twin for
a certain Lady at court.

(Nor did my glances give her any cause for offense,
but there was one night thick with moisture and smoke,
and, hearty in our cups—for they are great drinkers there—
we began dancing.
Topiawari's people first,
and we bent our backs trying their steps
to most comic effect,
for they fell about laughing.
Not her, though. She smoked and watched.

And in our turn,
we demonstrated certain dances of court and country.

And some how—*I do not know how*—
I found my arms around her waist.
I remember she steadied me with one hand
and with the other undid my points—
*I do not remember any more*—
just the drink and the fire and sounds of the river
and the smokey smell of her skin—
I awoke among my men.
I remember nothing else,
and perhaps I do not even remember that.)

We do not, will not touch their women.
For this we are loved.
And so we move among them like specters, fleshless and cold.

(She, among Topiawari's men, saw us off.)

7.

And so we have found a most bountiful land,
full of every lush and fruitful thing,
with gold sparkes in the stone and the ground,
Sparks which the Spanish call madre d'el oro

and we call the scum of gold,
a certain sign.

We fell to our knees
scrabbling with daggers and fingernails
to dig out that which is hidden
and finally release the tension of the hidden.
To do this, we lacked all necessary
save industry and desire.
And rather than chipping out gold
we left bloodstains leaked from ragged fingertips,
streaks which have by now, I am sure,
been washed into the river.

And so we must return
because *there is gold here.*

I am not so in love with noisome vermin,
calamitous storms, fetid disease, and other assorted ills
that I would wish to take on another such voyage
so far from home.
I am in the winter of my age
and want only to raise my son.
But it shall be found a weak policy in me
to betray the interests of my nation for my own ease,
And I pray her majesty will believe

the wealth of this land lies open to her,
to be taken by force or by friendship.

Guiana is a land that hath yet her maydenhed,
and so have I left it, undisturbed.

# THE MUSIC OF THE DEAD

## JENNIFER CROW

I hear voices—
the vast, slow swell
of a dream choir underfoot
sends vibrations
through my limbs
and shakes my certainties.

The song of angels
rises from wells
and cellars, quick-tempo
bells that dazzle
and fade into
the steady hum of soul-traffic
and the commerce of death.

Each step crunches
ice and bone, the percussion
of wasted lives stacked
in pyramids, corpses
frozen with faces touching.

The wind hushes
through firs bent under
winter's weight,
and this memory of breath
like an icicle
in the chest—

a jagged spear of hope
unfounded and unfound
in the slack blue-tinged flesh
too cold to stink,
features distorted
 beyond recognition.
I cannot hear her voice
in the bedlam of ghosts
and therefore
she cannot be here.

# THE DARK LADY
## MEGAN MESSINGER

They called her a whore before she died—now she's just "the bitch." But neither is ever said in LeBeau's hearing. Time was, he'd have spilled our guts on the deck for even looking cross-eyed at her. I should know: I was down on my knees enough bloody times, scrubbing at the planks. Now I'm not sure what he'd do. I guess it's just habit to step careful around the baron.

I, for one—and I might be the only one—remember her name as Carlotta. It's been a while, but you find the memories don't fade much. Of course, anything in a skirt gets to looking like a queen when you've been a few years out, but she was a real beauty. I first saw her bound and gagged, LeBeau's fist tangled up in all that thick black hair, pulling her head around so everyone could see what he'd got.

"Hear, hear!" I heard McCarthy mutter. "Hope he doesn't get selfish."

There was blood crusting on the corners of the dirty clout in her mouth. Her skirts were ragged up to the knees, and her blouse ripped as far as her waist, showing her neck, the lines of her collarbone, the mouthwatering strip of flesh between her breasts.

Her face was indistinct—we'd attacked as they were changing crews, and it was now after midnight—but Cutter's lanternlight played along her cat's cheekbones and the smooth curve of her jaw. Her eyes were closed, leaking tears that winked and sparkled, and her eyebrows winged up toward her temples, where soft hair curled like waves before being snarled and swallowed by LeBeau's fist. I adjusted the crutch under my arm and tried not to fall too in love with the girl. I couldn't guess whether her beauty would make LeBeau take a little care or whether he would lose himself in it. But dead in two weeks or dead by morning, she was the baron's plaything now.

He laughed and slid his gaze down her long lean body before speaking. "Cutter, everything off the ship and in our coffers?"

"Aye, sir."

"Wolfe?"

"Sir."

"Fire it." LeBeau turned his head and spat. "It stinks of Spaniards."

McCarthy sniggered and elbowed Diego in the ribs. Diego, not looking at him, calmly placed a hand on the flint-lock at the small of his back.

"Everyone back to the *Lady* unless you want an early taste of hell. It's going to burn like kindling, damn Spaniards are so oily." He laughed again. "Might not even have to polish my sword tonight. . . . Or maybe I'll choose to," he added, leering at the girl.

A laugh rose from the crew as they swung on ropes or filed back over the planks to *The Dark Lady*. I hung back, not wanting to get knocked off a plank and into the sea by accident. I felt LeBeau behind me before he spoke.

"You do so well by one dark lady, why not another, hey? Take her, clean her up."

"Aye, sir." Questions not appreciated.

He shoved her in my direction and waited for us to cross—the baron was always the last one back to the ship but for the fire crew, by his own tradition. I jerked my head for her to go first and held on to the rope binding her wrists behind her—though if she slipped or jumped, I couldn't have done much about it. Too busy watching the end of my crutch, placing it carefully on the salt-crusted, weather-beaten boarding plank.

But we did both make it to the other side. Amid hoots and hollers from the crew, who'd already broken out the palm whiskey and the new Spanish sack, I took her below to my workshop and sat her on my stool. I lit the lanterns and considered her for a long moment.

What was I supposed to do? I'd been a carpenter, bound for Sicily, when *The Dark Lady* looted and razed my ship. LeBeau had played cat-and-mouse with me for a bit before asking about the paint, ink, and varnish stains on my clothes—turns out he had been looking for a ship's doctor to doctor, he explained with half a smile, his ship. His lady. His lover, almost. So, newly crippled by a swift "security stroke," I'd set about polishing, repainting, scrubbing, and sanding. And here, where I mixed foul substances for paint and beat bullion into leaf, I was supposed to clean up a real woman.

Best start with the gag, which by now would be hopelessly woven in with her hair. I pulled a small carving knife from the rack in the wall and stumped toward her with it. Her eyes were level and unafraid as I stroked the blade along the gag, parting it threads at a time at the side of her face. Truth to tell, I enjoyed being so close to her, staring intently at a small patch of golden skin and inhaling something that was not quite a scent, but was distinctly woman all the same. The gag parted, and I peeled it from her mouth—she didn't make a noise, but the worn places began bleeding again. LeBeau wouldn't like that. Or maybe he would—I didn't know—and if he *was* displeased, it was Cutter who had gagged the girl in the first place, not I.

She worked her jaw while I worked the gag out of her hair, and when I tossed the clout on the floor, she turned to me and spoke. Her voice was low and rough—like a cat's tongue, like smoke—and I didn't understand a damn word of it. By the sound, she was switching languages every few words.

I shook my head. "English only. And if you're asking for help, you'd best forget that plan. Better your skin than mine, and LeBeau will kill you quick, if he does kills you. Me? Might take days."

35

She glared and said something else, something icy.

I shrugged. "Only escape is to jump or to drink, lass." I knelt with a bit of difficulty and reached for her blouse to button it up again, or at least see how many buttons were missing, and found myself laid out on the floor of my workroom, curled into a ball, sweating in pain. When I could think again, I realized that maybe I should have tied her feet to something.

"Look, you Spanish bitch," I snarled, "if there's anyone on this ship who's not going to bloody hurt you, it's me. So you can let me near you or you can face the winds as God made you, because after that, I'm sure as hell not untying your hands. *Comprende?*" When Diego got roaring drunk, he forgot every word of English he'd ever known and told long stories in his native tongue, stopping sometimes to make sure we understood. So I did know some Spanish, three or four words. The one she then leveled at me was one of his favorites, certainly.

I returned fire in the same language, and she nodded regally. Apparently the ability to curse was a letter of marque with this one, for she let me braid and pin up her hair, button her blouse, and wash the blood and soot from her face. I could hear the drunken dancing and the even more drunken concertina-playing from the deck. Crippled craftsmen not welcome.

I stood back and looked her over like a chair or bookcase. Little I could do about the ripped skirts, but otherwise, she

36

she barely looked like she'd gotten kidnapped on the high seas. Barely.

LeBeau's laugh drifted through the boards of the ceiling, and I leaned against the wall, waiting for the chance to get the beauty off my hands and myself into a hammock. I've been called half a man for it, and worse, but sometimes all I want is to go to bed. Alone. But if I had to stay up, she did turn out to be lovely company after that one misunderstanding. Like looking at a painting, it was.

Eventually she spoke again.

"English, love." I wondered if I could nip abovedecks for a drink.

The same set of words.

"Doesn't matter how many times you say it—I don't speak it."

Just one word then: "Carlotta."

"Your name?" I tried to think of the Spanish and ended up dredging some religion from my early days. *"Nomine?"*

She just shrugged and examined the floor. "Carlotta."

I tapped my chest. "Francis Nym."

She looked at me with an ironic slant to her perfect eyebrows and, in cadences I recognized as my own, told me she didn't speak my language.

"Nym," I repeated.

"Neem."

"Nym."

"Neem."

I shrugged. Close enough—itdidn't matter, anyway.

"Carlotta," she insisted.

"Carlotta."

"No. *Carlotta*," she said, drawing out the syllables, rolling her *r*, tapping the *t* on the back of her teeth.

"That's what I said!"

She smiled.

"You really are a vixen, you know that? I don't know if I'd marry you or strangle you." Not that it mattered.

A few more minutes of silence.

"All right, Carlotta. We're going to try something." I barred the door and took two knives from the rack: my sharpest and my longest. The long one I lay on the floor behind her, within easy reach, and with the other, I started cutting the ropes on her wrists. She froze like a deer, barely breathing, and once again made no noise when I pulled the fibers away from the wounds they had made. "Clean is clean. And the baron did say clean. And your hands are filthy."

The discarded gag became two thin bandages. I tied her hands again, but in front of her, crossed in her lap, the new ropes a few inches from my poor attempts at treatment. I didn't even have any booze for the girl, which was the only treatment I knew, anyway. That and burying a potato, if you got a wart.

A pounding on my door. "Who is it?"

"Cutter!"

"What do you want?"

"The girl! Baron says to lock her below. He's going to ransom her instead."

I wasn't sure what to think of that.

Cutter snorted. "You think any of us would play games with her? After the way he looked at her tonight? Don't want to spend the next week dying, thankye kindly."

And Cutter was LeBeau's toady to his rotten little core, of course. Nothing for it but to let him in. "Right, then." I lifted the bar from the door and opened it. "She kicks."

He licked his lips. "Does she."

"Carlotta?" I gestured with my head toward Cutter and the darkness that swam behind him. "Go with the nice gentleman."

She stood and swayed a bit. We looked on, Cutter likely at her breasts beneath the thin blouse, I not really willing to get close to her in case she took it in mind to kick me again. She was a good six inches taller than me, and probably outweighed me by a half a stone—most of that in curves and hair.

I closed the door on her strong, straight back, hung my hammock, blew out the lanterns, and climbed in. Tried for a minute to feel guilty or something, for sending her to a cell in the hold, but either I was more tired than I thought or the pirates' morals are catching, and I fell asleep.

I spent the next morning cleaning up after our little parley with the Spanish. No major work, just a lot of fiddling, and I was replacing a length of railing when I noticed it. A soft hum beneath my fingers, a little extra warmth to the wood. I ignored the feeling and went on with my work. Repairs done, I tested the joints by leaning on the new section, and as I pressed my palms to the wood, I felt the tingle rush into the new piece. I spat over the side and moved on, feeling uneasy.

*The Dark Lady* is an odd ship. Sleek, fast as you please, but crafty like a woman. I've got my hands on her all day, every day, feeling her every mood, so I think LeBeau's the only one who knows her better than me. Joke goes, there's a little round hole in the wall next to the baron's bunk. Never in his hearing, though.

If I had to say, I'd say she was pricking up her ears, keeping her eyes open, something like that. Every other second after I noticed it, I felt like turning around to see who was following me. It was maybe just a fancy of mine, spurred on by the way the baron talked about his ship, but I always thought of her like a person. Like our goddess, maybe.

But then, I've always been a drinker, so who's to say?

That afternoon found me dangling over the starboard side, sitting in a rope sling with a pot of paint in one hand and a brush in the other. The words THE DARK LADY took their wear and tear, same as the rest of us. Unlike on us, repairs on her were a quick enough job.

I had just finished the long swirl of the capital *D* when I heard my name. Looking up, I saw Evans's grizzled face peering over the rails. He grinned. "How's the weather down there?"

"Hot as your berth in hell and wetter 'n your sister on a Saturday night," I shouted back. "What do you want? I'm busy."

He spat over the side, just missing me, and grinned again. "Baron wants to see you."

"Wants to see me?" Hell. "Right, then, haul me up."

The ride back up was enough to spill paint down the front of my shirt and make my teeth rattle. Maybe I should have left off the bit about his sister.

I clambered over the rail, reclaimed my crutch from Evans, and turned around to find myself face-to-chest with LeBeau. Lovely silver buttons, he's got.

"You're a cultured little thing, Nym."

I couldn't tell if it was a question or not.

"Aren't you," he said pointedly.

"Aye, sir. A bit."

"I need appointments for a lady to be carved out this thing." He scuffed one black boot against the rough boards to indicate the ship.

"Aye, sir." I blinked. He never talked about *The Dark Lady* like that.

"And fitted out properly. Start now. List what you need." He started to walk away.

"Sir?"

He stopped but didn't turn.

"Some things it might be better for the lady to choose herself."

"She'll like what she's given," he snarled. A pause, and he added, " Ask Diego, if you have to."

I didn't think it would be wise to bring up the repainting of the hull.

Soon, it was all over the ship, thick and black as tar—the rumor that LeBeau was soft. Not out in the open, but when I hear a tale, it's sure that the rest of the crew has heard it ten times over. When she walked the decks, there was a dead silence over the whole ship. Every eye, every brush of breeze, every knot in the wood was turned toward her. I resented her because it was safer than resenting the baron, and because my workshop had been converted into her bower, such as it was. When a crippled carpenter and a half-blind old sailwright get to making curtains, it could very well be a sign that the ship's in a spot of trouble.

Which isn't to say that we gave up the business. The opposite happened, really. LeBeau directed attacks harder, more viciously, and with more daring than before. He whipped *The Dark Lady* into closer quarters, and more than once I saw him licking the blade of his long-handled knife. Sent a shiver up my bent spine, truth to tell, and I took to staying on *The*

*Dark Lady* instead of trooping over in the aftermath of an attack. No reason for me to be there, anyway—I never got so much as a bent candlestick out of it. And sometimes, when I stayed, she would come see me.

It was about a month after LeBeau had got her, and I was tucked into a dark, nasty little berth belowdecks. I'm sure I reeked of cheap ale, because it kept getting harder to get the damn stuff in my mouth and not all over me. Useless, useless Francis Nym. LeBeau seemed almost halfhearted about the upkeep of his ship. Didn't bother getting me any bloody paint or nails, that's for sure. Brocade and jewelry these days with him, and it felt that with every little job I did do, *The Dark Lady* sucked the life right out of me. Ship was hungry for something. Or maybe I was drunk.

Sure enough, the lantern burned right through my eyes and into the back of my skull. Drunk as a preacher on Tuesday, I cursed the lantern-carrier with a thick tongue and raised a forearm over my eyes. The arm with the tankard growing out of the other end. Bloody gone, all that nice cat piss wasted on my left shoulder.

"Neem?"

"Bleeding hell! Ah, damn me, Carlotta, go away. Go away, woman. Better alone and lonely than with a wreck like me." I felt my nose prickle and hoped this wouldn't turn into a weeping drunk. My head hurt something fierce already. "Go on."

"Baron attack," she said matter-of-factly. "Ship alone."

"Alone! Good. Ship alone, you alone, me alone." Cannon rattle shook the ship.

"Pffff."

I couldn't tell if she meant my logic or my sorry state. *"Go."*

She considered me for a moment, but her face was lost in the witchfire glare of the lantern. Finally she stooped and set it down before gliding away. It threw wavering bars of light across the gray walls that looked like teeth . . . like a woman's hair . . . like the slit-pupiled eyes of a cat . . . like strands of seaweed wrapping around me. And for all that, for all those bloody neck-tingling shadows and my bloody head and my need to just go the bleeding hell to sleep, I couldn't bring myself to blow it out.

The next night, LeBeau called everyone to the deck, even me. Still a bit hungover, I wobbled abovedecks and positioned myself in Foster's long shadow, a place where I could be seen by few and bothered by none. Except if LeBeau wanted to get at me for some reason, which I didn't think he would. I hadn't done anything wrong lately. I hadn't done much of anything lately.

Carlotta stood beside him, some of her hair drawn back from her face with silver combs, the rest of it streaming down her back and vanishing into the shadows of the rigging. Her dress—former bed curtains from an English captain's cabin—hugged her body up to the high lace neck.

I saw Wynstan lick his lips and resisted the urge to lay my crutch across his shins.

"Hello, lads." LeBeau grinned. "Pass it round—there you are."

The sack was making the circuit of the gathered men, and I couldn't decide whether my belly wanted the drink more than my head didn't. As usual, the drink won, and I found myself just standing there, holding a lovely cup of wine while the baron talked. Even Diego and Byers weren't sneaking sips, so I gathered that that would be a bad idea.

"Just look at us!" LeBeau barked. "Fat and drunk as kings, wouldn't you say? Luckiest damn dogs on the sea." He tipped his head a bit. "Never meaning to put you lot down, and you are a ruthless pack o' sharks when it comes down to it. But we never lived like this before, did we?"

Mumblings from the crew. He seemed satisfied.

"No! We never did." He kept speaking to us, but fixed his eyes on Carlotta. On her face. "There's some as say that a woman on the ship is bad luck. And couldn't she be a mermaid? But, no—*she's* our dark lady now!

"So drink up, lads." He lifted his own cup, still gazing at her. "Here's to my lovely bride to be."

There was the tiniest pause before a deafening "Hear, hear!" and a general guzzling of the drinks in our hands. But I saw uneasiness on the men's faces, and the carousing that night was a bit forced. Whatever the baron expected—revelry or massacre—it was best to hand it to him quick, and that we did.

My back and legs ached soon enough, and I figured it safe to slip below and into a hammock. No one would miss me. First I found Diego and returned his spare tankard, and as I was making my way through the crowd dancing on top of the hatch, I took one last look at Carlotta.

Stunning woman, I thought drunkenly. Lovely, really. Wish she'd smile, look happy, something.

But I cocked my head to the side and stole another gander at her. Calm, she looked. Not like a woman about to get married—or, hell, I didn't know what it was like to be suddenly engaged to LeBeau—but she did have the air of a figurehead about her, brave and quiet. She could be LeBeau's dark lady, the dark lady of *The Dark Lady,* which happened not to have a figurehead, just a little carved swirl like an eddy below the bowsprit.

Before I knew it, I was ambling toward her. LeBeau was off somewhere, and the rest of the crew was paying her no mind, as they were accustomed. I sat down heavily on the deck next to where she stood.

She looked down at me. "Hello, Neem."

I rested the back of my head against the railing. "Hello, Carlotta."

"You can walk?"

"Could, 'f I wanted. Going to bed soon, in fact. Just wanted to wish you a happy . . . a happy . . . erm . . . " I looked around. "You know."

"Wife, husband, wedding, marriage," she rattled off.

I laughed. "Capital! He could take you to England soon. No one'd know he stole you from a Spanish treasure hold."

"To England?"

"Sure. Nice place. Rains a lot." I tasted sea spray on my face. "Like this, but not salty." I felt another patter of droplets. "You know, I think the ship is moving more than I'm dizzy."

There was a feather-light touch on my hair, and she was gone. Below, I wagered. Men were running about now, furling up the sails and strapping down everything that wasn't already nailed. The sky swirled into a black squall between us and the horizon, extending cloudy arms that wrapped around our mainmast and reeled us in. I found I couldn't take my eyes off that dark gathering in the sky, couldn't run below for cover or even get out of anybody's way—McCarthy cursing me as he tripped over my splayed legs—even when the thunder drowned out the cracking of the mast and the ship tilted like a ladle into the sea. The grain of the wood was suddenly thousands of wiry hairs and sharp, angled fingernails, and I swore the howling of the winds was coming from the planks shivering beneath me with the strain of their motion, mercilessly driving us toward the black heart of the storm. My vision was red with anger not my own, and then it was snuffed out like a wavering lantern in a stark hold.

It isn't bad. Certainly not as bad as I expected, although I'll be damned if I expected this for myself.

Actually, it seems likely that this is damnation, but I can't be bothered to come up with new curses now, can I? I spend most of the time asleep, which suits me just fine. It isn't really sleep, though, not as I was used to it. It's like being raveled into the fading darkness, and rewoven when it returns at dusk. No dreams, no sense of time passing, just like the best of earthly nights. Rest of the time, I lean over the rail and toss the last of our hardtack to the birds, who are mightily confused when they snap up a morsel only to find nothing in their beaks. Wild enough to see us, not smart enough to realize what we are. I never realized before that a gull can look angry and confused at the same time, and that keeps me amused enough. I tried to keep the ship up for a while, but something about being the phantom terror of the high seas defies a new coat of paint or a good scrubbing.

Everyone else moves sharply through their shifts, same as always. LeBeau stalks up and down the decks, same as always, and every night we all gather—just like that last night—to drink tasteless wine in honor of the baron's love. A love that's reverted to his ship, of course. Funny how dead men usually haunt the living, but here we are, dead men being haunted by a ship that never really lived. Some of them mutter over it, say it's like having an extra ear or something, but I'm used to feeling odd things from this lady, and she's in much better spirits these days, as it were.

The other lady, we lost in the gale. As I mentioned before, the crew calls her "the bitch" in the minutes before we all melt away for the day, assuming that she's to blame for everything that happened to us and everything we became. No one really talks to me, same as always, except for Diego—in Spanish, mostly—and Cutter a bit, and certainly no one ever asks me a blessed thing. And I don't volunteer that sometimes, as I'm staring over the railing with a round of hardtack dangling from my fingers, there's a strong shape flowing alongside the ship, her curves scrolled into the waves and her hair spread around her like a dark sunburst or a gathering of clouds. I wave, and I think she smiles at me before scattering again into little scraps of shadow. It must be very still and cool down there, which, now that I think, maybe suits her better than we know.

# WHITECHAPEL AUTUMN, 1888

## ANN K. SCHWADER

No changing leaves lament the season here,
for nothing grows but woe in Mitre Square.
The belles of Ten Bells, numbed on gin & beer,
have small appreciation for this air
refreshed at last by dawn mists drifting cold
around the corners of St. Botolph's Church
where twilight draws the desperate & bold,
parading past on mankind's oldest search.

Yet summer dies in Buck's Row—not alone—
& Annie follows Polly down to dust
as cries of wholly simulated lust
are silenced by steel whispering on bone.
Their secret reaper rides a sharpened wind,
signing himself *your own light-hearted friend.*

# SUTTEE

## CATHERYNNE M. VALENTE

### I.

I have a sister.
Her body is made of corn.

Her eyes are apple seeds,
her waist a length of twisted rye.
And when the demon-king came for her, he
burst from the purple cup of the crocus,
and caught her by the grassy heel.

When our mother opened her legs,
my sister's head emerged first,
blonde hair matted with grapes
crushed against that muddy placenta
and olive-meat spattering her skin like henna ink.

I came second from the furrowed earth,
mouth stopped up with sugar and barley—
and such black hair, curled tightly around
my sister's fists.

When it was my turn, a golden deer leapt into a field
and bent its head—the clouds passed like water
over its burnished antlers—to nibble at fallen millet.
The men ran ahead of their spears to catch it, and I was alone
when the ten-headed demon Ravana
seized my braid like the lead of a dun cow,
and dragged me into the jeweled alleys of Lanka.

I sat on a red silk pillow
in the garden of the scab-haunched king.

She sat on a black throne, and the three-headed dog
dropped asphodel at her feet like meaty bones.

I watched the garden change,
and did not move when I was called.
Plums swelled up like bruises,
giving way to persimmons, orange as hanging lanterns,
and withered brown pomegranates, which
knowing those bloodied heart-seeds all too well,
I did not touch.

Snow covered the spiky pines,
and when oranges burned through the ice
an army of silk-snouted monkeys and men in horned armor
came clamoring through the fruit.

## II.

I did not go into the fire for him.

When the wing-footed boy came for my sister
in her wedding gown of peach-skins
she could not hide the red juice
dribbling down her thighs—
but no one called her a whore.
No one waggled their fingers inside her
to inspect the trailing spider-web of her hymen.

They ignored her mouth, loosened
with fruit and weeping.
They came marching down the shadowed stair
and told her to dress herself.

They were understanding—as all officials are—
but they did not let her go.

My husband built me a pyre.

His army of apes piled cedar on cypress
on camphor and rosewood.
The stink of it pricked my eyes.

*If you are pure*, he said,
*the fire will not touch you.*
*Then I will know.*

The monkeys cackled and struck stone on stone,
shrieking at the yellow spark.

### III.

I have a sister.
Her body is made of corn.

She would never have survived the fire.
Her amaranth calves would have gone up
like burning books.
And anyway, she is dead.

The demon-king touched his lips to her fingers—
her flesh froze blue and black.
He put his mouth to her navel—
her lips burst open like the mouth of a drowned woman.
And in this body, with all her grains rotted away,
she is wed for half the year.

It was for her I performed *suttee*,
for her I lay my body down

on the fragrant fire, over her cold corpse,
the one who could not get free.

Like a witch I fed the flames.
The sapphires strung through my hair
boiled and bubbled, trickling
into my eyes. I felt her round shoulders,
her slim arm around my waist,
each of her fingers a scald of purity.

All he saw was my gaze turned upwards,
the mandala of fire.
All he saw was my skin still whole,
my bones uncharred,
my hips smooth and cool.

IV.

I crawled back into my loamy mother,
hemorrhaging children.

He followed behind, stuffing our sons
into a reed basket, protesting loudly—
he believed me, now. He knew
I was chaste as an infant dove.

But he cannot find the opening.
Through the clay and the mud, I crept
into the furrowed earth and drew up my knees
to my chest. In the dark of my mother's body,
I sleep.

In the spring, my sister wriggles in beside me,
and curls my hair—such black hair!—around her fists.

# DIMINISHING

## TIM PRATT

You were my butterfly girl
white-winged and trailing flame
while the flowerbeds burned,
weeping over rare steaks
and empty rainbarrels,
walking roofpeaks like balance beams
and ghosting with the crows.

You were queen of pigeons and sparrows
and you could never rest
on the first floor.
You threw open all my windows,
put plants on the fire escape
and set a place for the moon at dinner.

You told me about monsters
and I read you stories
about gray-eyed girls
and clattering passions and how
to stop a stream in its bed.

You leapt off rocks and crawled
through windows and with every twisted
ankle you grew taller and surer of step
and I fell back, calling, crawling, stopped.

You made masks and paintings
and your eyes glittered
like sapphires or lust.

You spun farther away like satellites
and spiraled to the vanished point.

And, like autumn, you swung round again.

# THE TONGUELESS BELL

## CONSTANCE COOPER

The city gates are gagged with trees and breathless as the dead,
The mansions all are muffled now beneath a mask of vines.
Silty is the river lying smothered in its bed;
And mossy are the monuments among the muted shrines.

The brambles bite your ankles as you scale the sacred hill,
The holy grove holds out its hooks to graze and gouge your skin.
But still your hopes swing higher with each drop of blood you spill—
The chapel may be choked with weeds, but harbor gold within.

Here I hang, the chapel bell, still stately in my frame;
Though time has browned and lichened me, my iron still is strong.
O picture, pilgrim, if you can, my former days of fame:
The festivals, when folk would cheer the clamor of my song!

Alas, I am diminished since those days when I was young
And thousands came to hear my voice atop the temple knoll.

Can anything be sadder than a bell without a tongue?
Please, seeker, say you understand my yearning to be whole.
Come closer, if you pity me, and peer up from beneath
Into the iron hollow where the sharpened meat-hook hides.
I told you I was tongueless. But I still possess my teeth.
Ah, yes! Do struggle, please, my friend, and kick against my sides.

What joy, to hear your steel-toed boots boom out the holy knell
Just as it was on feastdays when the offer-chant was rung!
It was a thing of glory, then, to be a chapel bell
And sound each month at noonday when the sacrifice was hung.

Too soon, dear tongue, your legs will tire, your shrieks will shrink to moans,
Till only wind inclines you to bump out a hollow note
And later, only clinks will come from insubstantial bones—
Until they join the powder piled beneath my empty throat.

# FIX

## JEANNELLE M. FERREIRA

In life these people moved aside like leaves. Now they line the narrow steps down to all outbound trains and are as steady and sure as if someone set them here to guard not piss-soaked concrete but the door to the underworld. They will never get anywhere, of course, not New York, New Haven, New London or the small towns in between, where white wooden spires rise like bones against the night.

There are so many shades. They crowd and move and are passed through: a commuter moves his head with a jerk at the sudden cold, and then ducks down again, and nothing. No knowledge has passed from him into the shade, or back again. There, in the shadow of the great clock you can see them; in the flippety shudder of boards overhead, you can hear them mutter. Arrivals, departures, track, delayed, dead.

It's better, really, if you choose one. One story to know, one face to fix, or by the time the signal bells clang you will have been picked clean by shades who need. Yourself, you say you can't see them. You're more wrong than you ever could know. Maybe she looks like your lover, your best friend, that girl in black leather and tatters beneath the clocks. Maybe you looked up to capture what second it was in Rome, Berlin, and when your eyes fell again, dazzled with marble and light, they met hers —just for that second. You look at me now, alive and thick enough for baggage to smack into, and you can't stop blinking. It's all right; you're beginning to realize, now, but I knew before you.

I know why you gave the dead girl your dime: she looks like a jackdaw, but she wears your perfume.

I watch the girls, mostly. They're the desperate kind. Burning like gaslights and all of them wearing the way they died, lips cracked and blue and moving low over *please, please, please.* Some of them forget what they were asking for. Most don't. There are men here, too, but they belong to the dark corners, the passageways kept from the light by black-barred gates, and they forget faster. They whittle down to liquor-wetted rags, hunched, grimy and eyeless. You don't want to meet one; but they don't come up here. They forget we?re even walking overhead, and when the air rushes through the tunnels it spins them along like toys. It takes them a while to find the way back.

It's all right, go back. I'll hold your bag, if you want to shake out your wallet. Count the price of her passage before you've asked where she wants to go; try to press hands with her as she palms the change.

Cold?

Cold. Give me your hands. I have her story, if you want it; a circle, like most good ones. Moving so quickly won't help you. She has you already. She's with you now, beaten rook's hair and poor winter clothes, velvet and leather, spark and smudge. She'll follow where we're going, even if she has to make her way back again. It's in her eyes, how bright they are now, that last spark cupped and cherished in numb ungloved hands.

Mind the gap.

You've sat on your hair again. Did you think she would sit next to us, your pale passenger? She wants to see the harbor in the sunset; she always has. She came into this city for the first time as the water wrapped the sun in red for the night. The memory has never left her. Maybe she looks for her own face now in the scratched plastic pane; she smoothes one hand over it and she's trying to remember texture, remember that once she wore a ring.

She came here from a place where she never saw water; only fields laid out endlessly, in the way that makes people say they roll by; she thinks they more sort of swell, out across your line of sight and up and even beyond. She slept most of the way, the train shrugged her gently back and forth and she remembers it as the last real sleep she ever had.

She came for the education, and hers was a short one. He wasn't there to meet her at the station, and she had to step out alone into this soaring scatter of metal and glass. Down so far as she was, only five feet and some odd off the ground, there was no air on her face, no real air, nothing of the sky, only a gust that was gritty and hot. She had a bag, but suddenly she didn't, and with no money there was nothing for her to do but wait until morning.

Between one thing and another she never got where she was going. Maybe that's why she's still here, hiding in the fall of all that hair, sheltering herself as if it's cold. Oh, she got to the college, of course, and she painted grapes and cotton-draped men and much brighter landscapes in her spare time. Maybe college didn't suit her; maybe she wanted cramped studios, hard chairs and dim linoleum to turn into those fields she kept in her mind. She wasted, and longed, and he never came, and she ran away.

She came back to the station, because there was always light and heat, and because over the trains she couldn't hear those buildings moaning in the wind. She bummed cigarettes and drank cold coffee from cups left behind; she thought of tricking to scrape up her fare back home, but there's a knack to that, and she never had it. Though she doesn't ever remember being hungry, she got thinner as it got colder and she could no longer even pretend that somewhere above all those skyscrapers there was a sun.

And one night out on the platform she died, between cigarettes, and looked in the morning like something spun from blue and white glass.

Her name was Beata Greengage.

We change lines here. She'll go back now, you won't see her

again. That's what I hate about outdoor platforms—always cinders in your eyes, or bits of leaves, and how they water.

Revolving door! Revolving door. What made you stop like that?

Of course they're everywhere; especially in places like this, where the living move like fast, cold water. Where the lights never go out. Where you can always see the last deep spark in their eyes.

This isn't heartbreak; this is a feast.

# COUNTRIES OF THE SUN

## SONYA TAAFFE

*I: In the Shadow of the Walls*
    This story you told
    with lapis lazuli on your lips,
    histories and epithets crushed
    dark-blue between your teeth
    as though you had eaten the sky entire,
    sun that rides in justice and his father
    moon who reels the day behind him,
    to write yourself over, inside and out,
    with hymns to every god and hero
    that ever this intricate city praised.
    The weight of time on your tongue
    like inlaid bronze and copper,
    cool as stone that soaks up words
    like rain on thirsting earth,
    nicked and tapped and sectioned
    into meaning: you whom I needed
    to unriddle, syllabic mysteries
    and floodwater revelation, before
    I could taste the tale myself
    as I set it down anew.

## II: *Knots of Heaven*

Some nights she dreams of the texture of his hair: dense as pelt, fine as a newborn child's. It slid through her fingers like reeds clustering up beside water, like harvest grain, like the aureole mane of a lion. He fell to earth in her arms, naked as clay; his breath sweetened her mouth with green, tufted grass and tamarisk, while she taught him all she knew best. Her body has remembered him exactly, when she wakes.

Some nights she dreams of him clothed in drought and feathers that trail in the darkness at his feet, his mouth stopped with earth and no words written on its blank slate. Not even her name, that first rough and sinuous caress of language about his tongue on which the dust has settled thick as centuries; not even recognition rises up like smoke through a crack in the shadow, and she wakes cold as the morning star fades in the dawn.

But some nights she dreams of his eyes, dark as her own, and how she watched his own name welling up inside them as he rocked inside her that seventh night. The tide of himself that flowed and broke: and he knew her as he knew himself, as he knew *star* and *cedar* and *city* and *sun* and *desire* and all the things for which he had yet no word, like *death*. With her hand she brushed his man's hair one last time, soft and wild, and from this dream she wakes smiling and crying together.

*III: Dragonflies*

You filled the offering bowls
like talismans against the dark,
propitiating the ghost of your
own fears. When you spoke
of love, I heard only loss: dry
decay and dissolution, the unclothing
of corruption from the bones
and your own twinned skull staring back
at you: the dead are beautiful
only in memory. Your other gone
to ruin and ceremony, cedar
forests and bull's bloodied horns
childish night-frights against that
pragmatic truth: to this, you too.

*IV: Carnelian in Flower*

Gems choked his throat like grief: no solace
in grapes that click like agate counters on the vine,

clusters of smoke-black obsidian, dates of lapis
pendant among smooth chlorite leaves, the gleam

and dazzle of fruit made for no human mouth.
Blind for immortality, he walked sunwise

through jeweled groves and left behind him
the gods' orchard on the far side of the dark,

wonders on its boughs, unliving, undying.

## V: *Where the World Runs Out*

The boat rides heavy in the water with the weight of the
living, hero-flesh that has its own gravity to bend the sun's
favor, shatter apotropaic stone, walk out of the world until time
harrows his face like a man who has done nothing but travel
since creation began.

This sea I have voyaged since before my own memories
began, that only the sun crossed unscathed to the oldest lands,
retrograde where rivers begin, where time healed and halted
over the ancient scars of inundation: these waters I know like
the palm of my own callused hand, this country beyond the
world's impossible end: I am no wise man.

He will not find what he is looking for.

## VI: *The Dead Without Dust*

I saw him, I saw him,
sleepless above the earth,
his bones bare to the sky.
I saw him, I saw him,
his chariot-wheels splintered,
the lions at his throat at last.

Wind and desolation
stalk the streets that built
his name; prayers fall
like stones to the world below.
No one, no one saw him.
Roasted grains and beer
he would scrounge from old dishes,
but his ghost never came home:
only mourning and misfortune,
only this tale.

## VII: *The Old Young Again*

These words you have worn long enough.

Clay, stone, a new tongue raveled for each listener; papyrus and parchment, your coat of story sewn to wear till it hangs in scales and threads; ink and phosphors, where time wore the walls to earth: ancient as dust, evergreen.

Cast off this skin too.

# ESCAPE

## RIO LE MOIGNAN

Striving for the sun, time blurred
like the slow running of wax,
moment into moment: an imperishable arc.
Heavy years ahead,
Earthbound as any mortal man must be:
he soared,
shrugged off the weighted thought,
let that future go, unheeded as his father's pleading.
The wind numbed him,
until he felt the wax blistering his back.
The sea so far below gleamed richly and he rose.
Scorched feathers drifted around him.
A falling flight, payment in full
for freedom, a choice made from self-knowledge.
His father's tears were lost in the salt water,
and the waves were flecked with feathers.

Even the plummet held the memory of soaring,
but Icarus is famed for hubris,
remembered as a fool
by men who have not flown.

# MEDEA

## SARAH KOPLIK

When I fled my father's house
My younger brother asked to come along
How could he have known what was coming?
We took him
Part sibling, part hostage for our safety
The beautiful captain and the maid.
But my father
Did he know the seriousness of my resolve
Chasing after us over the wind-tossed sea?
So what could I do
My brother died peaceably enough
And I scattered his body across the water.

It was then He spoke,
Not before,
Tearing frantically at his hair
"Oh my darling, my Medea,
How . . ."
He fell silent and turned his face from me
And I knew he could not understand.

You will say I had no heart
To kill as I did
But the king was an old man
And a fool.
And my children;
I never touched him
You understand
Easier to drag my own flesh down to Hades
Than see his golden eyes grow dim
His skin fall from his bones
His mouth stop moving
In helpless anger.

# MIRANDA

## JOSELLE VANDERHOOFT

the blood egg startles her
with its redness.
not like ladybugs
or strawberries,
these she understands.
instead she thinks it's more
like the color of the bird
the cat left in her sheets.
wriggling in bed after her snack
she felt it—squish—
against her big toe.
puzzled, she lifted the duvet
and gasped
as if she looked upon a death's head
made to resemble a broken shell.

when Mother snapped the black plastic lid
down on the carnage
she hid her face between fingers
still sticky from a ring pop,
as if her chipped nail polish

could protect her from the day old smell.
and yet the stain remained
even when she washed her hands
and forsook the cotton candy pink
for purple glitter.

it's still there now
or else, it has come back
sharper and redder
somehow intestinal,
a pisces of a stain,
the color of bruises
and pain.
it forces her, insect-like,
from her skin
into some strange new body made
of circles not of squares.

in this cocoon of flesh,
bed sheets and panties
she transforms
acquiring a new joint at the waist—
or so she thinks
as she leans down
to investigate the insides of thighs
swollen like honey dew

or a very ripe peach.
"oh brave new world that hath such people in it"
her hands caress her knees
excited but so scared
as she looks deep into that gaping hole
in search of the dark seed.

# THE SHAPE OF MISTAKE
## LAUREL WINTER

### 1. Past

You were shy,
your guts cramping in the company of strangers,
but I sent you to the market to consult the spirit woman.

"Have charity," you pleaded,
but I turned my face away, launched you down that slope.

Details spin in my mind;
your gray dress, the way you chewed your hair.
A feast of innocence, you were.
Had I valued you more, that night might have never happened.
They lured you into a fine home,
grand as glass, filled with every comfort.
Clean, polished, lavish—so unlike this dim hut.
A ram the size of a bull lay on the table.
They bid you to eat.

You were the discovery of the season.
They wrapped gold around your arms,

filled you with potent wine.
"What is your answer?" they asked,
having never given the question.
"Yes," you said.
Your humble design melted within you.
They lifted your gray dress and gowned you in green,
set your feet on a trail you had not imagined before that day.


I finished planting the winter wheat,
waited for you to ride up to the house we built together.
Your turkeys gobbled in unison, a strange, eerie song.
I felt weak, didn't know why.
"Save me," moaned the wind.


I took the leather whip from the cabinet,
wrapped myself in a shawl you knit.
My center shook.
I found your horse,
ill-tended, chewing its bit, before the great house.
"Save me," it groaned.
The end, I thought.
My bones changed to fragile glass, the whip to a wisp of grass.
We had lived clear, quiet lives, but that was over.
I felt a fork twist in my heart.

Above me, through the windows,
their eyes stared down, steady, amused, knowing.
You danced with shadows, your shoes worn through.
"Tomorrow you may have her back," I heard,
though their lips did not move.
"If she will go."
The sun sank low behind the mountains,
taking light and warmth into some dank cave.

You left for the south the next day, the butcher told me,
your color high and your eyes blank.

The winter was mild.
I wandered the mountains under clouds that held their dreams
tight.
Deer came to the salt block but I could not shoot them.
The farm kept me well enough,
though the kitchen was spare when the spring storms trapped
me.
A jaguar killed the turkeys.
I could not reach town to replenish the stores.
I sewed torn shirts with your needle,
awkward stitches that did not truly mend.

## 2. Present

Cold rivers run from the edges of snowdrifts,
but my heart does not melt under the weight and warmth of
spring.
Time. Endless. I rage against the youth that inhabits me.
Only work succors me, even when I do it wrong.
I dreamed you held a key in front of me.
When I reached out, you swallowed it.
I dreamed you rode a mustang down a road that led nowhere.
I dreamed you played with a tiny ball;
it bounced from your hand—and it was your heart.
*How do you fare with these others?*

Our house—my house—is small and empty.
I knead dough until it is tough.
Nothing is new but the emptiness.
*Are you intrepid now? Fast? A gem in their hands?*
The bread bakes crisp and dark while I am wondering.
Again, I have made enough for two.

I exclude myself from company,
turning away from a wrangler traveling through,
rugged and beautiful, but not you.
*Do you dress in high style?*
I hibernate no matter the season,

a winter bear at heart.
*Do you dance to a strange tune,*
*wear lights in your hair,*

*wrap your slender form in blue paper?*
I write you letters on ribbons and release them into the wind.

I inhabit a place where sleep sends pictures of you
wheeling through my dreams like fallen stars.
You are the daughter of love, gone to the edge—and over.
My heart teaches me the meaning of moment,
the shape of mistake.
Days add up, beads on a string of sorrow.
I wrap the beads around me and they become my skin.

Until I see you,
pale and wild, laughing at nothing, drunk on their liqueurs,
I will have no resolution.
Or until you come back to me, shorn of memory or fleeing it.

*Please come back.*
I write it on a ribbon, let it go.

# CANVAS, MIRROR, GLASS
## HOLLY PHILLIPS

Nicolas bought Isobel a new dress to wear to the opening at the Galerie Fayette. His other gifts had been small things, a new book, a sheaf of watercolor paper. This elegant silk made her wonder: was she a kept woman, now? But she didn't know how to refuse it, and it was beautiful. She pinned her hair in a chignon and put slender gold hoops in her ears (a present from her father before she left home) and in the mirror caught a glimpse of someone new, someone false, someone sophisticated and serene.

The canvases were all of lumpy women, some shrouded in gray and dun washes, some exposed on barren plains with awkward horizons. Nicolas looked with care, but Isobel knew he would not buy any of them. He was possessed of a politeness that almost amounted to kindness at times. She liked him for it, but felt pity for the artist, Michelle, who watched him with such hope, although Michelle was not an easy woman to pity. Aware of those eyes, Isobel could not bear to look at any more drab lumpen female forms. She drifted away from Nicolas's side and was not surprised to find Didier soon at her shoulder.

"I could paint you in that dress," he said restlessly. "Against a window looking out on the sea."

"There is no sea in Charmondy," she said. Didier had been plaguing her to sit for him almost since she had met him. "Why don't you ask Michelle? Everyone says we're twins."

"No, Michelle still thinks she might become an artist. Besides, she burned out her light long ago. It's only you I want to paint, you, like a fire in the darkness, like a candle in the night."

"No," she said, smiling, embarrassed.

"I would paint Michelle only as your shadow."

She shook her head.

Didier gave an irritable shrug. Before he could speak, Michelle herself was beside them. She said, a challenge: "So?"

"Don't ask," Didier said. "You know you never listen."

"I would listen if you ever told me something I could actually use." She turned to Isobel. "What do you think?"

Isobel had learned this lesson in art school. "Ambitious," she said. "Risky."

"Crap," Didier said. "Don't muddy yourself with lies, Isobel. Real art deserves truth."

"So at least it's *real* crap?" Michelle said to him.

Didier replied with an indifferent, "Yes."

Michelle's face blazed, and for a moment Isobel thought she was going to hit him, but then she turned on her heel and stalked away. Isobel blushed, as much for being caught in a lie as for the other woman's pain.

"God," Didier said, his gaze hot and dark on her face. "Let me paint you, this is driving me crazy."

"No."

He threw up his hands. "Will you let me get you some wine, at least?"

"Yes, thank you."

"Yes, thank you," he mocked her. "You and your school-girl manners." He cut through the crowd to the bar. Isobel looked around for Nicolas, spotted Michelle leaning against the wall between two big dull canvases. With her eyes lowered and her mouth compressed she had the look of a Renaissance saint, brighter in her anger than her paintings. For once Isobel saw the resemblance people always commented on. They shared the high forehead, arched brows and long, hooded eyes, the narrow nose and secretive mouth. Michelle had a stronger chin and thinner lips, Isobel had a shining curtain of heavy blonde hair nearly to her shoulders. They both had the dark blue eyes, opaque, like slate wet with rain. It was this resemblance that had granted Isobel an instant "in" with Didier's crowd, that otherwise scorned tourists. She had never pretended to be anything else. Her talent, great or small, she carried with her as secretly as her snapshots of home.

Didier, burning with vision, indifferent to critics, resentful of the great Masters who had learned all his lessons before he was born, was the bonfire that warmed and sometimes burned a whole circle of people who met and argued and struggled to learn. He, his talent, his restless energy, drew students and acolytes, would-be peers and hangers-on, and a few wealthy patrons like Nicolas Kurlow who bought paintings, paid the café bill, and took a young Isobel home to the white stone house on the rue des Chevaliers. He was too old for her, Nicolas. Too old, too sophisticated, too rich. She finally saw him by the bar, tall and cool, graying-fair, listening to someone she couldn't see. Then the crowd parted and she could: Didier, gesturing, a glass in each hand.

Nicolas said sometime soon after that, perhaps even later that night: "Why don't you let Didier paint you?"

"I'm a primitive." Nicolas was cool against her, taut beneath her hands. "He's a camera and he wants to steal my soul."

Nicolas drew the sheet from her body. "If I could paint like Didier . . . "

"No, no!" She covered her face with her hands.

"I would. If I could." Longing caught at his voice. He kissed the fingers that hid her eyes. "Isobel, be honest."

She lowered her hands and folded them primly above her breasts. "I am always honest with you, Nicolas." She liked to say his name in three distinct syllables: Nee-koh-lahs.

"Then tell me why."

"Oh, there is no why. Why should I want to?"

"There is always a why."

She turned her head on the pillow. "Maybe I don't want to see how he sees me."

"I know how he sees you." Nicolas rose above her, leaned with his fists planted either side of her shoulders. "He sees you as I see you. He would paint you as I would paint you, if I could paint. Isobel—"

"No," she said, moved by instinct, not reason.

"—if I asked—"

"No."

"—would you let him—"

"No!"

As on most days, when Nicolas had gone to his office she put her sketchbook and a novel in her shoulder bag along with a bottle of water and left the big house on the rue des Chevaliers. There had been a little rain in the night, and the morning was sweet. Even the antique buildings smelled good, pale sandstone that breathed a riverbank cool. At the tram stop in front of the post office, a flower vendor had set up his cart. The scents of violets and narcissus mingled with car exhaust, but it was the colors that drew her. Yellow and cream daffodils, tulips in three shades of flame, early van Gogh iris, blue and gold. The tram was slow to come and she could not resist; she bought a bouquet of sunny daffodils and sat with them on her lap as the electric trolley-car labored through poorer streets to the top of the southern hill.

She knocked on Didier's studio door, received no answer, tried the knob. The door swung open onto his stairs. No voices from above. She closed the door and climbed the three dark flights to the lofty studio.

She had only been here once before, with Nicolas, and she had forgotten, or had not noticed, the first impression of air and light. The house was high on the steep hillside. Paned skylights in the attic roof looked up and out onto mountains and sky, and only secondly down on the town fitted neatly into the valley below. Isobel stood at the top of the stairs with her flowers in her hands until the studio itself came into focus: tables, shelves, chairs, canvases, stools, easels, frames. Didier. He stood with his back to her, foursquare to a large canvas on an easel, and said without turning, "What do you want?"

She caught her breath, unsure of the answer.

He twisted around, at first without moving his feet, then turning completely when he saw who it was. "It's you!" he said. His dark face brightened, his arms opened for an embrace. She held the flowers between them, but let him kiss her cheek. His shoes were paint-spattered, but he smelled only of coffee and clean clothes. He wasn't working. "So Nicolas convinced you," he said.

Nicolas had not said he'd already spoken to Didier. She had not told Nicolas she meant to agree. The portrait was supposed to be a gift, a generous gift in return for all his generosity, not an accession to his and Didier's plans. They had been conspiring against her.

Didier failed to notice her sulkiness, or perhaps he noticed and did not care. He put his hand on her waist and said, "Come in, I'll make coffee, we can do some sketches and I'll prime a canvas tonight. Michelle, you should throw your brushes away and use the palette knife for a year."

"And have you accuse me of trying to copy your technique?" Michelle rose from a chair that had been hidden behind the easel; the canvas Didier had been studying was one of hers. A featureless human outline was being crowded by angular shadows. Isobel understood what Didier meant. The image was flat, the shadows hid nothing, not even the weave of the linen they were painted on.

"Hello, Isobel," Michelle said.

"Hello," Isobel said, embarrassed as well as sulky, now.

"You see?" Didier said. "She never listens. What's the point of asking if you never listen?"

"You're the one who should listen to yourself," Michelle said. "Every day you say to do the complete opposite of what you said the day before. Last month you said image, not paint. Now you say paint not image!"

"Are you so limited you can't do two things at once? You think a painting is all what's in your head and not the actual, physical stuff on the canvas? Or what's on the canvas, but not what happens in the viewer's eye? Even if you can't encompass everything, at least fail by trying!" He threw out his arms, then turned the gesture into a sweeping away. "Come back when you have something new, if you ever do. I'm going to be busy for a while. I hope you like your coffee strong," he added to Isobel.

"Yes, thank you," she said, politely, which made him hoot. He strode to the back of the studio where a stove and fridge huddled to either side of a deep, paint-stained sink. Michelle gave Isobel a sullen look.

"I suppose you agree with him."

"I don't know enough to agree or disagree."

Michelle shrugged, contemptuous, and did not argue. She slipped the canvas into a battered folder and gathered up a coat and a purse. She didn't say good-bye to Didier, but she surprised Isobel by pausing at the top of the stairs to say, "Come for coffee sometime. I'll show you what I'm doing now."

"Thank you."

"Mornings are best. Didier can tell you where." She hesitated, as if about to say more, then shrugged again and left without another word. Didier came from the back of the studio with two mugs in his hands.

He said, "Sit on the big chair there under the skylight and take off your clothes."

"I will *not*," she said.

He laughed, handed her a mug. She took it and sat where

he wanted her, dropping her shoulder bag and laying the daffodils at her feet.

Michelle seemed surprised to see Isobel, a sort of stupid-looking surprise that made Isobel wonder if she had misunderstood the invitation. She looked at Michelle, nonplused, and Michelle stared at her, the two women standing on either side of an open door. Then Michelle shifted, and stepped aside so Isobel could enter.

"I was working," she said in explanation.

"I'm sorry," Isobel said. "You said the morning."

"Yes. It's good. I'm glad of the break." Michelle closed the door and led Isobel inside. There was an unlighted passage, then another door. The studio seemed bright after the dark hall, but it didn't have the high brilliance of Didier's place. Three sash windows looked onto a mossy courtyard and the neighbor's back wall; two large canvases propped on easels caught much of the daylight as it came in. The air smelled strongly of turpentine, despite the sash raised on the farthest window.

"I won't stay long," Isobel said.

"Is Nicolas expecting you?"

"No, I just meant, I won't keep you from your work."

"Oh, it doesn't matter. According to Didier it's all only practice anyway." Michelle spoke with such an accustomed bitterness that Isobel was silenced. Michelle didn't seem to notice, or care. Like Didier, she kept a kettle in her studio. She set about making coffee.

Isobel had not much wanted to come. She had never felt comfortable in Michelle's presence, put off by the woman's manner and perhaps by the way everyone exclaimed over their likeness. Isobel, privately, did not enjoy the comparison. Michelle was tall and heavy-boned, with big hands, and rough skin she tried to make smooth with cosmetics and cream, and the deep voice of the habitual smoker. Isobel was also tall, and had spent much of her adolescence suffering the certainty that she was too big, too clumsy, insufficiently feminine. She knew she was more finely made than Michelle, but even making that distinction was enough to reawaken insecurity. She did not watch the other woman arrange filters and mugs.

There were a good many paintings on the walls, most of them large, all of them in the same flat, dull style as the nudes in Michelle's show, though they weren't all figures, there were landscapes and still lifes as well. There was a rattan couch made comfortable with cushions and shawls, a tall lamp with a fringed shade, file folders stacked on the floor, no shelves or tables except the one that held the familiar litter of paint tubes and brushes and bottles and rags. The view out the windows, of the courtyard paved in crooked slate stones patched and bordered with moss, the back wall with its high blind windows and a drainpipe that stained the aged yellow

stucco, gave the room an air of secretive, melancholy aban-
donment. It was not an unpleasant feeling, but not one Isobel
would have associated with Michelle.

"It's more than I can afford," Michelle said.

Isobel looked around to see that she was being observed.
"I like it."

Michelle lifted a shoulder and tilted her head, part agree-
ment, part deprecating shrug. "It's nothing like Didier's, of
course."

"His studio is so big and bright, and that view? I don't
think I could paint there. You'd have to be very confident,
and very good."

"Ha. Confident *or* good." Michelle turned to pour the
coffee into mugs. "Sit down. I'll show you some sketches if
you like."

Isobel let her bag slide off her shoulder and sat on the end
of the couch, on a fat blue cushion sewn with tiny mirrors.
"Yes, thank you."

The coffee was black, and hot. She sipped, then bent to set
the cup on the bare floor, her tongue a little burned. Michelle
rummaged on the table for a couple of small sketchbooks
that she brought back to lay in Isobel's lap. Isobel picked one
up and Michelle said, "No, start with the other one," and sat
down beside her.

Line drawings done in soft pencil. Michelle drew on both
sides of each page, and sometimes, as if to further conserve

paper, she drew two or three images on a single sheet, juxtapositions and even overlays, like a double exposure, that were sometimes very strong. An old man's face over a flowering branch. A weathered gravestone, a butcher's hands on a joint of meat, the delicate mask of a sleeping cat. Isobel was struck by the fineness of both the sensibility and the line.

"These are very good," she said, and blushed because she was afraid Michelle would read her surprise.

Michelle sipped her coffee, her gaze on Isobel's face. Isobel set the first book aside, opened the other. Her fingers hesitated over a face she knew, another acquaintance in Didier's crowd.

Michelle said, "Why did you change your mind about sitting for Didier?"

Isobel looked up, startled.

"I'm sorry," Michelle said, "is that a question I shouldn't ask?"

"No, of course not. Why shouldn't you?" Isobel looked down at the sketchbook, turned a page. "It started to seem a little silly, that's all. Always saying no."

"And Nicolas asked you to."

Isobel turned another page. Another face she knew.

"Would you mind if I took a look at some of your drawings? Did you bring your sketchbook with you?"

Isobel startled again. She hadn't realized Michelle knew about her drawing, it wasn't something she advertised, but she could not refuse with the other woman's work in her hands. She fished in her bag and handed over the book.

The room was silent but for the uneven rhythm of turned pages.

Nicolas was in Michelle's book, his eyes lowered, his face cool, aloof, self-contained. Michelle had given him a priest's collar and Isobel was shocked at how well it suited him: she had come very quickly to think of him as a sensual man. She turned the page, and found a series of hands, gesturing and lying still.

"Ah," Michelle said.

"They're only studies." Isobel did not lift her gaze farther than her own book on the other's knee.

"Only." A page turned. "I could see a whole series of oils, all these windows and doors."

"No," Isobel said. "I don't paint."

"Why not?"

She looked back at the book in her lap. "I'm not ready." Turned a page.

"You can't learn how to paint by drawing. There is no ready."

Isobel did not reply. Under her hands lay her own face—or was it Michelle's face as she had glimpsed it the night of the opening, the saint's face? But no, it was hers, almost sexless in its burning intensity. Isobel blushed. That face was a face she had thought only Nicolas had ever seen. She covered the eyes with her fingers, then closed the book, though she had not reached the end. She looked up to find Michelle watching her.

"I think Nicolas was right," Michelle said. "If I were him, I would want Didier to paint you, too."

Isobel shook her head, letting her hair veil her face. She was too embarrassed to speak.

"Didier's good enough to make a masterpiece out of you. Good enough, obsessed enough. But still," Michelle added, "I'm not sure you were right to agree. Men like that can be dangerous, you know."

Isobel did not even know which man Michelle was referring to. Nicolas? Or Didier?

He had primed the canvas, sketched a rough cartoon, blocked out the color. Isobel was still learning the pose, the view, the way he grumbled and laughed in commentary on the work of his eyes and hands. Thinking of Michelle's sketches, Isobel tried to watch his hands, wondering if they were the ones Michelle had drawn over and over again, but he scolded her for changing the angle of her head. He had decided not to use the chair. He set her against a wall, cool plaster beneath her shoulders, her head leaning back to emphasize the line of her jaw, the heavy lids of her eyes. She didn't mind standing. The intensity of his regard was harder to bear.

"Ah, ah," he said, "you're hiding. Come out, now. Be honest."

"Honest! How am I not being honest?"

"Don't move."

"Why does everyone keep telling me that?"

"Don't move!" He snatched at a brush. "Who is everyone?"

"No one."

"Ha! Nicolas. What are you hiding from him?"

"Nothing!"

"Don't move."

He slathered blue on with a broad knife, stepped back, cut some yellow in. By sliding her eyes a little to the side, Isobel could see other canvases of his stacked against a wall. He did not hang his own work in his studio. From a distance the depth of space and color rivaled the view of the mountains and town, bright as that view was with spring light, but near to, Isobel knew, the pictures would fall apart into heavy streaks and ridges of paint. He danced as he worked, a formal dance, forward and bow, back and turn. She stood against the wall, and did not move.

He said, "Tell me there will be others."

"Others." She was tired. This was near the end of a session.

"Other sittings, other paintings, other days. I want you in the heat of summer, outside. I want you in the winter, under the glass in the winter rains. Rain, and those eyes. Give me those eyes again." She did. He looked hot, his jaw rough with beard, his body jittery inside his clothes. "Do you ever wonder where Nicolas found the courage to ask for this? I don't know that I could. He has a collector's passion, a curator's soul. Which does he want more, I wonder: your portrait or you?"

"When you're done, he'll have both."

Didier grinned a dog's grin, sharp-toothed. "When I'm done. I might never be. You change with the light. Isobel, I want to paint you when you're fifty."

As he had placed her, most of her weight was on one foot. Her hip hurt, her knee. Something in her shoulder creaked. She moved.

"Not yet. The light is still good."

"I'm tired."

"One more minute."

"One?"

"Five."

The light he wanted was the morning light that glanced through the upper windows, illuminating only the air and a slant of wall above her head. There was no clock in her line of sight. When she felt sunlight on her face, she pushed away from the wall and stretched, rubbed her face where her loose hair had tickled, arched her back so her spine could remember how to move. When she looked, Didier was standing before the canvas studying her with a hungry look—the painted her, the unfinished one.

"It isn't enough," he said. "I want you in the evening, too."

"No." She started towards the lavatory. "Nicolas gets the evenings."

"Was that irony?" he said, raising his voice as she closed the door. "Isobel, I don't want you ironical yet!"

Isobel kicked the bottom of the door. She was beginning to understand how Michelle felt, always angry at Didier, always coming back. She did not like his eyes. She did not like how, after a morning under his gaze, she went back to the house on the rue des Chevaliers and felt herself hiding from Nicolas. Hiding what, she could not have said. Neither man ever told her what they did or did not see in her. When she had washed her hands and splashed cold water on her face, she came out, went to stand beside him to look at the day's work. Didier was not a coy painter, he did not mind if others saw the work in progress, but she didn't really understand what she saw. He seemed to change the mood of the painting every day, even as he slowly brought out the detail in figure and face, background and light. He worked the whole canvas, sketching over and over and over with thicknesses of paint. She witnessed the stages, and waited for the revelation.

"Admit it," he said to the canvas, "you are a little in love with me, too."

"You aren't in love with me."

"Aren't I?" He smiled. "But I meant, as well as Nicolas."

"Am I in love with him?"

He turned to look at her, but she had bent to pick up her bag, and her hair covered her face.

"Stay for lunch," he said.

"No." She shook back her hair, in possession again. "I'm meeting Michelle at one."


"So how is the work going?" Michelle asked once they were served with bread and wine.

"I don't know. I'm not sure I understand how he works."

"Not the portrait. I meant your own work."

"I don't work." Isobel was hungry. One sip of wine flushed her cheeks. "I'm a kept woman, didn't you know?"

"Isn't it odd," Michelle said, for once taking the lighter mood, "how poor men have lovers, and rich men have mistresses? It doesn't seem fair, given he isn't even married. Or is he?"

"Not that I ever heard." Isobel rocked her glass on its stem, scowling at the pale wine that rested almost still within the moving bowl.

"My, Didier has put you in a mood, hasn't he? What did he say?"

"Nothing." Isobel sat up, drank, let herself fall to her elbow again.

"He'll say anything to get you to look how he wants you, and he'll want something different every day. Oh, I know the type."

"Is he a type?"

"Isobel, do you mind if I ask how old you are?"

Isobel rocked her glass. "Twenty-four."

"Older than I was."

Isobel opened her mouth, but then the waiter came for their orders, and there was never another chance—Michelle never gave her another chance—to ask.


A collector's passion, a curator's soul.

Nicolas took her out of the city on the weekend, to an inn in the mountains where there were wildflowers, a creek, a famous gorge. The inn was old, with stone floors and white walls hung with watercolors, mostly landscapes in yellow and blue. The lawn was an uncut meadow; there were old, crooked pines, and gravel paths that led to the gorge's rim where guests could walk above the deep, tremulous roar of the creek in flood. The whole time they were there, Isobel felt Nicolas watching her, her expressions, her movements, what she saw, what she felt. She shut her finger in a drawer and he winced.

Such close attention seemed to put a distance between them. In bed she felt pressed, manipulated, overwhelmed. Betrayed by his knowledge of her, by her own inability to deny what he knew, she tried to turn her anger into passion—to turn his own passion against him—and it left him astounded, even shaken, watching her with pale eyes gone dark with redoubled desire. Yes, still watching. She bent over him and covered his eyes, so that he came in the darkness of her hands.

On their second morning, they had breakfast in the cool dining room whose open windows made the other guests' voices sound sleepy and remote, then walked again to the gorge under a rain-scented raft of clouds. Isobel wore a heavy cream wool sweater she had brought from home, her hair loose about her face. Nicolas wore a black, high-necked shirt. In the diffuse light, against the damp stone walls of the gorge, above the black collar, his face was the priest's face in Michelle's book. Isobel stopped and said his name.

He looked at her, his face lightening as if she had just arrived and he was glad to see her. "Yes?"

She shook her head, at a loss.

"Isobel." He paused, tucked a strand of her hair behind her ear, then took his hand away. "I've been thinking lately that I may have pushed you too hard about the portrait. You don't seem very happy about it."

She shook her head again, her gaze on the foaming water below. "It's all right. It just tires me out, you know?" She tried a smile. "Didier tires me out."

The spring thaw boomed between its walls, the wind combed the grasses, a finch sang from the top of a pine.

"Isobel," Nicolas said gently, "is there something you want to tell me?"

She looked at him and realized she was seeing the cool, reasoned, ardent face of jealousy. It made her laugh with surprise. "No."

His face darkened, tightened: no longer the priest's face. He looked down to the water. She went to him and put her arms sweetly about his neck.

"Nicolas," she said. Nee-koh-lahs. "Which do you want more, me or the picture?"

He put his hands on her back, not a rejection, but neither an embrace. "You," he said roughly, angrily. "More than you want me."

"How do you know?" She leaned back to see his eyes. "Didier wants the picture more."

He studied her face, and slowly his arms came around her. "Does that mean he won't sell it to me when it's done?"

She laughed.

The canvas was six feet by almost four, the portrait nearly life-sized. Painted Isobel leaned against the wall, her bent knee turned a little to the side, her arms hanging loose, her hair framing her throat. White throat, white shirt, white plaster: white made from a dozen colors of light and shade. Live Isobel leaned against the wall and forgot what colors she was, forgot Didier's dance, forgot Nicolas's eyes. He was there, taking a morning away from the bank, and perhaps it was his presence that relaxed her enough so that she could dream. Blue sky blazed above the valley and the town, the mountains made green folds against the horizon, a background deep enough to hide secret gorges, streams, lupines with leaves like hands to capture the dew. The foreground was the window, the sloping wall of rippled panes in iron frames, dusty from past rain, pigeon flocks, city air. In her dream, Isobel solved the problem of how to paint the glass, and what lay beyond the glass, and what was seen through the glass, without losing continuity, or separation, or depth—Her eyes went white with sunlight. She blinked first, and then moved.

Didier growled.

She mumbled something back at him, rubbing her eyes with the heels of her palms. When she took them away she saw Nicolas sitting in the chair behind the easel. He watched the canvas as Didier worked with a fat brush, worked fast before he lost his train of thought. Isobel walked past them to the lavatory. Standing at the mirror above the sink, she thought, There are moments, there are moments . . . But today she just looked like herself. The mirror needed cleaning. She yawned, drank some water from the tap, looked under the sink, but there was nothing to clean it with. She went out again. Nicolas was looking through the paintings stacked against the wall while Didier rummaged in the refrigerator.

"I have cheese and apples and" something that got lost in the depths of the fridge.

"That's fine." Isobel stretched and walked, swaying, her

hands still locked above her head, to where Nicolas stood looking at several small oils, very rough and alive.

"Are these studies? Have you worked from them?" he said to Didier.

"What?" Didier took his head out of the fridge.

"Are these studies?"

"Those. No, they're not anything." After he said it, Didier looked more interested and walked over, a green apple in each hand. He stood by Nicolas and scrutinized the pictures in question.

"They might be," Nicolas said.

Didier grunted.

Isobel took one of the apples out of his hand.

"There's cheese," Didier said.

"Thank you."

He snorted, but went on looking at the pictures. Isobel bit into the apple and wandered over to the easel. Without looking around, Didier said, "I forgot. Michelle dropped a note off for you while you were away.

"For me?"

"It's on the table, I think." He jerked a shoulder, perhaps in the direction of the long refectory table that held the clutter of paints, brushes, coffee cups, jars of oil, bottles with the dregs of wine. Isobel was looking for a letter, a fold of paper or a neat envelope, so it took her a while to consider the small sketchbook propped against a tin of turpentine. She picked it up, then had to set the apple in its place so she could turn the pages. There were the faces she had already seen, Nicolas and herself, and the hands. Whose hands? Some man's graceful hands. After the hands there were a few penned lines as careful as a schoolgirl's.

Isobel read, the taste of apple gone sour in her mouth, and felt blood rush into her face, her fingers, her ears, and then away again. She closed the book, found her jacket and her purse, tried to put her jacket on without letting go of either sketchbook or purse, put the book in the purse, put her jacket on.

"Isobel?" Nicolas said.

"I have to go."

They looked at her, two men, they might have been strangers, faces known from sketches in a book, illustrations of astonishment.

"Isobel!" Nicolas said, but she ran down the stairs, down the hill, and there was a tram just stopping at the bottom of the street.

*I know you*, the letter said. *How I know you, like I know myself. You think it was never done before. A man painted a mask for me once. I spent half my life, my whole waking life, trying to take it off and show what lies beneath. Trying to be whoever it is that lies beneath. And then you come and it is you. It is you. And you are letting him paint the mask again. I can't bear it. I won't. I won't live through that again.*

She and Nicolas had been gone the whole weekend. She expected horrors. She expected death.

Michelle lay as if asleep on the rattan couch, her face pressed to the blue cushion sewn with mirrors. Her dark hair was lank, her mouth slack and crusted with vomit. The cushion was stained. There was a wine bottle, a glass, an empty bottle for pills. But Michelle breathed, she breathed, a sickly expiration that made Isobel sit on the floor, her head on her knees, dizzy with relief. When she could she found a telephone, called for an ambulance. It did not occur to her to call Didier's studio, Nicolas' house. They were quite absent from her thoughts. She found a damp rag and cleaned Michelle's face. Vomit and cosmetics wiped away to reveal a young man's heavy bones, the fine red-blond bristles of a day-old beard. Isobel put the rag in the sink, sat down on the floor by the couch and held Michelle's hand. Michel's hand. It was the long, strong, graceful hand from the sketchbook. In the great expanse of her relief, her release from guilt, these realizations came quite gently to Isobel. Not so much a revelation, as an understanding of something she had almost known.

The ambulance men came and took Michel away. She washed the glass, scrubbed the cushion. The mirrors grew bright again, but the nap was ruined. The telephone rang. The sun fell bright into the courtyard. Through the windows the moss glowed like emerald, the back wall like butter, the slate flagstones like Michel's and Isobel's eyes. When the telephone was quiet, she found her bag and Michel's keys so she could lock the door. Her hands shook a little, a long way off, on the other side of her relief. Relief seemed too small a word for this expanse, this expansion, this buoyancy of spirit that was so utterly undeserved. She put Michel's keys in her bag, where they rattled against the keys to Nicolas' house, and began to walk. It was sunny and warm. A cat sunned itself on a window ledge. She did not know where she was going at first, but Michel's note had not ended with a farewell. Rather, with an address. She thought at first it was the name of a church, Saint Michel's, but it turned out to be a school.

The painting hung in the assembly hall.

As in a dream, she had not had to ask. She would not have known what to ask for. But the priest who met her in the entrance hall, with his shaved crown and neat black cassock, greeted her as if he knew who she was, and showed her where to go almost without saying a word. The vast distance of her relief, if relief was what it was, protected her from surprise. From small surprises. The painting was not a surprise. It was the revelation. Saint Michael with his foot on the dragon's neck, spear in hand, face shining with God's grace. The saint's face, neither man nor woman. The boy's face.

"He was a student," the priest said. "You might be his sister."

"Yes," she said. "Who painted it?"

"One of the brothers here. We used to be renowned for our art and music programs. He had a tremendous talent, as you can see. It was a great loss for the school when he left."

There was a wealth of story in his voice, a whole saga full of shadows and light. Isobel did not ask. She did not feel it was anything she wanted, or needed, to know. The painting was enough. She looked a while longer, declined his offer to show her the chapel. Said her thanks and went politely on her way.

The late spring evening was near by the time she regained the top of the southern hill. Rich light cut through the upper panes of glass, a false ceiling above the shade of Didier's studio. No one was there. Isobel ran the tap until it grew cold, then drank two glasses of water. She was thirsty after the long walk. She used the telephone to call the hospital; Michel's condition was stable. When the nurse asked her if she was a relative, she said she was Michel's sister. The woman said the staff psychiatrist was usually called in for "cases like these." Isobel thanked her, hung up, stood at the window to watch the end of the day lift itself out of the valley. The great luminance of her relief seemed to follow the daylight, lofting above her, leaving her shadowed, tired, and small. Her feet hurt. She leaned for a moment against the wall where she posed for Didier, then, finally, went to the easel.

The saint's face, the woman's, the girl's. All the shades of white glowed in the gathering dusk, the ivory of her skin, the gold of her hair. Her eyes were luminous against the luminous violet sky. Her knee bent a little, but both feet on the floor. Nothing in her painted hands. Her real hands had picked up a knife off the table, the one sharp enough to trim canvas with, but she set it down again. She was not Michel. She could wear this mask if she chose. After a bit she took the portrait from the easel, and in the last, the very last light of day, set up a new canvas and from memory began to paint the window and what lay beyond.

# THE STRING

## AINSLEY DICKS

the string, so sylphanous, that pulls the vertebrae into a line
and ravels out
to spool down to the coccyx

the ambergris of vein:
a ferrous fragrance
permeates the skin—all crystalline—like brine

the ribbing, once encrusted,
rusted like an old doubloon
barnacled-over
rivets in a still-contracting chest
to scrape against the flesh

crustacean half-moon of the hand—
impacted, opalescent,
knuckled-down—it coyly shuffles its chatoyancy
coiling about the neck

the crown (now molluskan, serrated,
nacred-out)

secretes itself a molar-faceted fascia,
corrugates a denser crenellation
draped with dental crescents

the tubercle of tongue
nimbly inflects its beveled rim of aggregate carbuncle
turning in

the string of syllables that spills, verbatim, from the spine
from many mouths:
the moule, and cockle-shell

# THE RELATIONSHIP BETWEEN LOVERS AND WORDS

## JAIDA JONES

*"Times like these. Someone is writing and we are only words."*
—*Xai*

### I. Bergamot
*a small tree*
there you were beneath it and lifting one arm up,
throwing one arm back,
in a Venetian garden (I think;
the details are unclear now, muted nouns)
and reaching for it, stretching and reaching,
while the strangest nakedness bathed your body, softened by sunlight.
I thought:
if only I could paint you as you are
in my deepest of dreams,
*with sour citrus fruits.*


### II. Astrolabes
*a medieval invention*
plotted the course of our stars today; jokingly,

we listen to the fortune teller who says
'You were alchemists in a life past,
but I do not know if you were lovers
or enemies'
as she plotted the course of your hand,
the lines drawn zodiacally
*to determine the altitude of the sun.*


## III. Chrysoprase
*an apple-green chalcedony*
lay there imagined in the hollow of your neck
where collar-bone met collar-bone,
the smooth white and the gemstone like a beetle
burrowing against you;
like Egypt, your beloved country,
and the distance between us desert after desert,
and the touch of your skin a cool Nile against my skin,
and the flash of your heart like a buried beetle
*used as a gemstone.*


## IV. Marjoram
*aromatic plants*
each a reminder that I should know how to smell you
how to trace your scent
with my lips, how to touch it
with my breath,

how to spread you against me
like a delicacy,
or let you grow without my help,
in a garden I am not the first to imagine
*with small bruise-white flowers.*

## V. Windjammer
*a*
time ago, a long time ago,
(for you believe in past lives and inherited lovers,
karmic intervention as opposed to divine intervention,
that I have slept with you before, many times
and will sleep with you again, many times
though we may not sleep with each other
this time around)
we sailed together, you explain, beneath the storm-swirled sky
from Italy to somewhere
(the somewhere did not count;
we drowned the third day)
on a
*large sailing ship.*

## VI. Windlasses
*a machine for*
every task and every purpose: this is our place,
to design, to machinate,

to mechanize appropriate mechanisms.
And so you too have allowed yourself to be useful,
you have designed this oblique cylinder
and have raised my heart bastioned upon it like
*raising weights.*

## VII. Marten
*mammal related to the weasel*
I may not be, but still you hunt me,
and each day wear a new piece of me around your neck
*with a slender body, bushy tail, soft fur.*

## VIII. Damascened
*metalwork*
in these ancient days:
bowed over books I, transcribing with crying quill,
and you, in the fire of the forges,
dirt upon your cheeks and heat upon your hands.
Somehow despite this I have come to understand
that then you were building me, and I did not know
how intricate the detail,
*decorated with patterns of curling inlay.*

## IX. Estuary
*where the sea*
is lapping, lapping, lapping,

and you and I are simply napping
my head upon your easy breast,
a storm is brewing in the West.
And one of us is singing, singing
to the water, bringing, bringing,
elsewhere bells are ringing, ringing
the salty water stinging, stinging.
(What comes of this? my lover queried;
time beneath the ocean buried.)
And here our twenty fingers quiver—
twilight comes and
*meets the river.*

## X. Garret
*a room*
hid us. We were only children.
We were only dirty-faced children.
We were only uninspiring children.
Still, we gathered old coal like buried treasure
and painted our faces black and blacker,
pretended we were chimney sweeps
and with an old broomstick I felt in love with you
though I forgot not to die three months later
of a cold caught
*on the top floor of the house, typically under a pitched roof.*

## XI. Haymow

*a pile of hay*
a clear, cool day—I bring you your dinner,
you eat it slow. Here, we romp and rut
and leave smelling like animals
raised
*in a barn.*


## XII. Belvederes

*pavilions or towers on top of a building*
where we looked out at the world spread all-ways around us
here there was mist,
there, a rising sunlight and a red sky,
to the left of us the stables,
while to the right of us the hills rolled on and on
like a graveyard. (And, if you followed them long enough,
you would come to the graveyard.)
It is not a clear day, but we can see forever up here,
*commanding a wide view.*


## XIII. Sirocco

*a hot*
day and an unlucky number. What words you have picked!
you say;
and what fruits you pick as you say it.
Would that we were better with peaches;

still, we are devouring figs.
Such is the landscape. Such is our current predicament.
Almonds, dates, and oil-lamps.
(I will dance for you, I promise,
I will dance for you and when the last veil falls
I will be nothing more than one noun,
your noun.
Such is the fate of man.
Such is the fate of a devoted lover.)
It begins to blow over us all,
this fate,
this
*humid southerly wind.*

# OUROBOROS TIME

## YOON HA LEE

Twining, not twinning;
no amphisbaena, you
circle in Möbius
splendor. Alpha,
omega. All times are
one, the end
begun, the clock still-
born, nonorientable
nonpareil.

# BRILLIG

## RICHARD PARKS

"'Twas brillig, and the slithey toves—"

*Brillig brillig brillig!*

That's one way to beat the poem. Start repeating words in a random selection. Breaks up the rhythm, you see. It's the rhythm that's dangerous. Don't ask me why but I know I'm right. The words may *seem* dangerous, mysterious, eldritch, and all that, but they're just stuff and nonsense. Learian. Charles Dodgson would know what I mean. I don't know if he realized what he had unleashed, but he did know about Edward Lear. This isn't Lear. It's Charles Dodgson, Lewis Carroll, and it's Jabberwocky. Lear is safe. At least, I've yet to find a demon in Lear, probably because I stopped reading him ages ago. Fear. Fear of Lear. Pity, as I do miss the Jumblies. Their heads are green, their hands are blue. They went to sea in a sieve, you know. Marvelous. Still, can't risk it. One demon is quite enough.

Jabberwocky.

Vorpal swords ultimately useless. The creature is always slain but it's never killed. Gallumph all you want with what-ever head you think you've taken, but it's so. The Jabberwock always dies but Jabberwocky always lives, and the monster is merely part of it and not even the most important part at that.

Jabberwocky is going to destroy me, I know. I don't know when or even why, but I do know how. Sooner or later the arms weary, the walls are breached, the sentries sleep. The poem wants me to recite it. I won't. It can't make me. Not again. Third time is magic. Third time's the charm. After the third time the drowning man is seen no more.

"Twas brillig—"

Hah. Thought it would catch me napping. Not that easy, you serpent of scansion, you coil of gyres and gimbles. Slithy as a tove, I elude thee once more, mimsy and outgrabed. So what if the Jabberwock haunts my dreams? It can't hurt me any more than I can hurt it, for all that I carry its head back to my father every night. My father with the empty face. He doesn't hug me. I'm no beamish. There is no chortling. Just the blood-painted sword and the smiling head of the monster, and my Father's face that has neither mouth nor nose nor eyes. Father is symbolic but doesn't have much else to do. He doesn't need a face. The Jabberwock does, to mock me. There's an efficiency in dreams; probably has to do with not being real.

I keep coming back to my father's face. It's silly. I know who he is. I know what he looks like. I don't remember him at all, growing up. Strange if I did, since he wasn't there. But I've met him. He's a man. Nice enough in his way. Nothing special. The Father in my dreams has no face. Tenniel never drew the father's face. The son, yes, the Jabberwock, yes, even the borogoves, but the Father? Nothing. You think that's a coincidence? I don't, because there's no such thing. Tenniel knew.

I do remember the first time for the poem. Not for reading it; I read it for years, off and on, along with Dodgson's silly book. No, the first time I recited it aloud. I don't know why I did. Fresh out of college and starting my life. New job that I was just getting to know, new fiancee, ditto. Stressful, but good. Busy. Feeling fey. Loved the feel of the words off my tongue. Brillig. Slith toves. Gyre and gimble. Frumious. Once I'd done it that first time, my only question was why I hadn't done it before. Reading is all well and good, but those words, those weird and wonderful words, they want to be spoken. Maybe they need to be spoken, I don't know.

That was the end of that job. My first. Oh, they *said* it had nothing to do with the poem. Bad fit. Not working out. Interests not congruent. Mysterious, potent, eldritch words, but not the poem. Doing my job while it was my job, learning my job while it was my job, but saying the words.

Oh, bandersnatch . . .

"Twas brillig, and the slithy toves did jump and frizzle, mom's a babe . . . "

Okay if you change the words a bit. Did I say that out loud? The rhythm, it wants me to forget, but I won't. The rhythm, that's what does it. Sets up the echoes in your head and they go to work. As I said, dangerous. Gotta be careful. The words want to be spoken only because the sounds want to be heard, so it's not the words. They don't mean anything, I know that, I said that. Have to be more careful. Musn't . . . well, clear enough what I musn't, and that's that.

The second time I said the poem, I lost the fiancee. In my defense I didn't understand before then. I didn't know. Thought the job was a fluke, my bad luck, and I still had Jenni. Then I didn't. The poem came out as a sort of song that day. I hadn't said it in months, not since the job. I was still looking. I still had Jenni. Everything was good. The poem took that away, and now I'm all that's left. I know what that means now, but not then. Then the words came out of me in a little song and Jenni told me there was someone else. That was it. Happens millions of times a day, all over the world. Someone else. Don't love you. Not sure I ever did. You're weird. That's when I knew. Once is a fluke twice is a trend. Three times is history. Tried to tell her, make her see the words, hear the way I heard. She got frightened, ran from me. Ran. From me.

" . . . all mimsy were the borogoves, and the mome raths . . . "

Did something unnatural to a hedgehog. There. Further than I've gone in a while but not too far. See? You won't beat me. I can stop any time I want to. I can say the words but not all of them, and the spell or curse or mystic vibration never happens. Won't let it happen and you can't make me. I'm in charge, not you. Never you. And yes, I whistle past grave-yards too. Why do you ask? Just to make music for the dead things there, you understand. You never know who or what might be listening. The poem taught me that.

"Oh, frabjous day! Caloo, callay! He throttled his bok choy."

Damn, don't know why I keep changing the words. Doesn't help. Once I even thought of referring to Jabberwocky as "The Carroll Poem" the way actors refer to "Macbeth" as "the Scottish Play" but that's just superstition. "Jabberwocky" is real. And when was the last time I got to that part? Can't remember. It doesn't want me to. Or I don't. It hurts not to feel the words. Like a junkie missing his smack. I'm shivering for lack of a word, a sound, a rhythm. Uffish thots. I knew I was having uffish thots, of course. Always do that at brillig. And after. That's when you put water on for tea or start broiling dinner. Tea and dinner are always good. Brillig time comes early, stays late. Welcome, brillig. Suppose they couldn't find any? It always happens. There's no tea here. Just brillig. And a pair of toves. Slithy. When the bandersnatch shows up, I'm leaving. Where? To nowhere because, well, there's nowhere to go. Nowhere to go where I am not, therefore nowhere Jabberwocky is not.

"Twas brillig and the slithy toves did gyre and gimble in the wabe. All mimsy were the borogroves, and the mome raths outgrabe."

124

That was just the beginning. That's all right. I can recite the beginning as many times as I want. It's just a coincidence that the beginning is the same as the end, like an ouroboros swallowing its tail. Always the beginning couplet, but never the end. How can I tell the difference? Because the ending couplet comes at the end, silly. So I didn't recite all of the poem, I didn't! It was the beginning.

I swear I didn't do it.

Don't look at me like that, Father. Don't look at me with no eyes. But he does, they all do, all those things that don't really exist. But most of all Father, symbolic, always missing, always present, shunned. Shun the frumious bandersnatch. I do beware, I do shun, all my life I have shunned . . . I did not say the words, not to the end, the real end. I went back to the beginning. I always go back to the beginning. Always. Nothing's changed! Start over, always start over, never end. Never.

Why can't I go back?

Father doesn't answer. He just smiles at me. It's impossible, you know. It's all impossible.

He has no face.

# ARACHNE

## THEODORA GOSS

She plays upon her web as on a lute.
The spider that you trapped beside the wall,
The common or garden Brown, with one red spot,
Uses the same technique, enticing flies
By plucking a string with one furred foreleg. They,
Hearing vibrations, enter and are caught.
As she is to the elementary Brown,
Her infinite variations to his one
Simplicity, so is her song to his.
This is what she will sing you, if you dare
Go from this village up the mountainside,
Where olive trees wither in the endless sun
And empty streambeds wind toward the sea,
Up to her cavern, filled with echoing sound:

*Your cheeks are bronze like cymbals, comely boy,*
*Your shoulder blades spread like a falcon's wings,*
*You are as fresh as water in which mint*
*Has steeped all morning on a shaded stone.*
*There is a wine produced in Attica*
*Like honey on the tongue, like molten gold*

*Proceeding down the throat, that cannot match*
*The burning sweetness of my poisoned kiss,*
*And Aphrodite on her flowering couch,*
*Woven of honeysuckle and wild rose,*
*Cannot embrace you as my eight arms can.*

You will stand silent while the echoes sound;
Then you will walk into her shining strings.

# BEAUTY SLEEP

## HELENA BELL

Sleeping Beauty dreamt of falling,
teeth rotting, dancing naked
at her own coronation.

She learned to fence, ride bareback,
mountain climb and duel with Counts
(the limitations of her sex unknown to her,
as the prickly briers creeping along her walls).

The vengeful witch ensured
nightmares were a bother:
not snapping shut with the tiger's jaws,
the canyon floor or saber's slice.
SB began to dream of pain,
as well as color: the werewolf's eyes
white as moonlight, and fangs
stained red by her shoulder tendons.

She took up flying, bow hunting,
magic. Charmed snakes
to delay the spiders, while hurling

spears at dragons.
One by one the monsters died,
pain dreams quelled. Faces emerged:
friends, dead relatives,
and they conspired to dream together.
Take trips, build cottages.
Raise families—except SB
who occasionally dreamed of princes
(all girls do) wondering how a life awake
would compare to the satin sheets
she conquered.

# BEANS

## JANE YOLEN

Jack, you see, went hand over hand
To a land beyond understanding:
Streets paved with gold, gold bedstands,
Gold bidets, golden harps, golden geese,
Eggs the color of wedding bands.
He hated being poor, having jack all.
So he stole a gigantic load, jacked the big man.
Has-been no longer, he unhanded himself
Down the beanstalk, fled home, kissed mom,
Drank a quick cup of something strong
Made from beans, then chopped down the stalk.
Sometimes a boy hits the jackpot,
Becomes a man with one lucky whack.
Believe it. Would a story lie?

# THE TRICKSTER IN MY BELLY
## ERZEBET YELLOWBOY

Maybe tonight isn't the time, now that there is a trickster in my belly.

I gobbled him up, swallowed him down, all his hairy little legs tickling and swirling in my throat until he landed there, deep inside. It was not an unpleasant sensation and when it was done, I had changed. If I were at home, they'd steam him out over hot rocks, but I'm nowhere near home and now that he's in place, I don't want to go anywhere, but I promised her a visit. I'll keep him tucked away in my secret place and pretend I never ate him.

A cool, clear sky stretches out above me and I'm driving down a road surrounded by wide, green spaces and fluttering grasses and in the distance I can see clouds gathering and preparing for their long trek over the darkening plains. My destination is a small house neatly segregated from the road by a thicket of trees and in it lives an old woman with hair like night. She'll tell me how to live with this secret, for I believe she has one, too, though I had planned this trip long before I ate him.

My wheels are spinning over blacktop and birds dart out

from the edges of the pavement, flit past my windshield, oblivious to my swerving and braking; they don't care that I care not to see their feathers on my windshield. Grasshoppers hit the headlights, are crunched beneath the tires and tonight's moon is palely visible over the bluffs I've left behind. I put my hand on my stomach, feel the pressure there of those eight legs creeping through my gut. Ahead, a car has stopped, flashers on, and beside it stands a man who might have known me long before I ever wanted to be known.

I ask him, "Do you need help?" He says yes, he's run out of gas, and I say okay, we'll siphon some of mine. I pop the trunk while he looks at my long legs, bare under a simmering red skirt, and I'm buried up to my hips in spare tires, jacks and flashlights, all the litter of every trip I've ever taken. I reach for a hose I keep just for such a circumstance and in my grasping, my hand circles the jug of water lying on its side. I smile as that tiny secret twists around to watch. The man can't see me kneeling beside my car as if to pull that foul liquid from its bowels. He can't see me fill his gas can with water, clear and scentless, but he watches when I rise and pour it in his tank. His eyes disturb me, black and brown and piercing and I throw his can onto the ground and speed away, laughing with the creature in my belly at the trick.

The clouds are moving closer and the road is stretching thin, tar exchanged for gravel. I hear something hit the roof, I turn the dial on the radio and hear the warning that a storm is rolling in. I do not care, I'm laughing and driving and the music is thundering out the open window and ahead I see another car stopped by the side of the road. This time it's a woman who might have said something to me long before I ever understood her words. I stop again and ask, "Do you need help?"

The woman says yes, I've lost my wallet on the other side of the road but my eyes are blind and I can not see to cross. I put my hand on her shoulder and gently guide her into the road. I feel the legs twitching, the secret crawling and hear it whisper in my ear. I lead her to the other side and round a bit and tell her here we are, and that I've put her wallet on the seat. I leave here there, on the far side of the road, and we laugh together, trickster and I, as I head out on my way.

I'm driving away when it hits and I'm pummeled by hail stones as big as my fist. I see the hard metal above my head denting with each stone that falls and laugh at nature's fury and her bliss. Soon enough the rain's so thick I can not see a thing and so I stop the car and light a cigarette. I'll wait, I tell myself, until it passes. I'm very close and I know the old woman will be there, no matter when I arrive.

Afterwards all the world is dented, all the grasses flattened and the gravel shot aside and even the clouds look as though they've been fractured by the hail. Raindrops glisten in the last light of a lately sinking sun, covering the plains in a layer of diamonds and where the dirt shows through, it seems as though a wide gold setting is holding all in place.

Another few miles and I'm there at the border of trees and it's too dark now for me to tell what kind they are. I park at the side of the house and walk up to the door, stepping through mud and soggy flowers, puncture vine that's lost its bite and ivy that covers her steps. I knock and feel a grumble in my belly. I go in.

She's standing by the stove in the corner of the room, putting a pot on the fire. She turns and smiles at me and her hair is fanning out along her back. Her eyes are bright and she tells me to get her some turnips from out back so she can make us a soup. She tosses me an apron and I tie it on, though not too tightly for I don't want to suffocate my secret. Out behind her house there is a garden and she has timpsila and sage and a bunch of liquid plants that I don't recognize and the stars are just bright enough for me to see. There's a stick for digging and I pull up two or three bulbs, remembering the taste of the timpsila soup my grandmother used to make. I feel a scratching at the back of my throat and glance about at the rocks strewn here and there in the dirt.

Into my apron I pile ten rocks, no larger than golf balls, and over them I lay the timpsila. By the water pump I rinse them all and then I go back inside, where she is waiting. She watches as I drop the goods into the pot and pick up a spoon so that I can stir them. "Smells good," she says and tells me to add more wood to the fire. I do and soon that soup is smoking and my little friend is laughing because the old woman's dinner is made of rocks. I'm stirring and the water is boiling and the old woman is watching and steam is rolling out of the pot and over my head and sweat is gushing out of my pores because she's added more wood and the fire is blazing in the stove's belly.

I feel faint and she's watching as I sway back and forth, but I can't stop stirring because she has her eye fixed on me. Soon I start in coughing and choking and I'm gasping for breath and she's doing nothing but watching me as I retch and finally fall onto my knees, bent over in front of her so that all I can see through my watering eyes are her shoeless feet. I feel like a cat, rasping and choking out a massive ball of hair onto the floor. But it's not hair that comes out of me.

She strokes my back as I bend there, hanging onto the wood floor with my nails, scrabbling for breath. She holds my hair away from my face and smiles at the trails my tears have made in the dirt on my face. I feel him coming up; he can't withstand the onslaught and my traitorous body will not hold him down. I'm crying now because I don't want my secret to be revealed, not like this, not in a sweaty mess on this old woman's floor. I think I can not take any more, I feel my whole insides wanting to come out my mouth and then she hits me, squarely on the back, and out it comes. I will not look, I tell myself, though I can hear it hit the floor and I think that he is heavier on the outside than he ever seemed within.

She pulls me up, carefully, gently, stands me on my feet.

The smoke has bled out her open window, the room is clear and cool. She holds out her hand, palm up, and on it I can see a pebble, no bigger than a thumbnail. It's round and white and glistens with my spit and it takes a minute for me to understand. I look at her and she's smiling, her lips curled in amusement, the scent of soup on her breath. She hands me the pebble and I don't want to take it, but she's got her eye on me again and there's little else I can do.

I hold it and turn it round and round, searching for its legs and eyes and mouth but there are none of these things. There is only this stone. It is perfectly smooth, it went down in a gulp and she looks at me with cobwebs in her eyes and says, "You've been tricked."

I look at her and shrug, and put the stone into the hollow of my tongue and swallow. The spider drops from her eye into mine and she is gone. I turn and stir the soup and wait, our secret safe until the next one comes.

# ARBOR LOW
# (ANCIENT MONUMENT IN DERBYSHIRE)
## ELIZABETH WEIN

Shin-deep in mud and dung, the bleak yard ends
and the green wastes begin. A crippled stile
crawls over the low wall; a cardboard arrow
dispassionately points the way, a narrow
track that traps sheep in old green quirks and bends
back from the mound to which it leads. With guile
and grass and earth, the hill hides in its bowl
a perfect ring of stones; some squat, some lean
and tall, a graceful circle in the clean
cold air, an old forgotten shrine alone
on the cool moor. The sharp, sweet scent of coal
smoke on the wet wind hovers here and lingers,
the only tribute still sent to these fingers
of grasping, broken, green and ancient stone.

# NEW YEAR'S EVE AT WEST KENNET
## SARAH SINGLETON

A seven-veiled sky—
Skeins of mist and curd,
Clod and gauze,
Slide on the distant blue face.

The air's savour,
A stew of earth,
Old straw and standing water.

The spring is a dead mouth,
All swallowed up.
The drab willow flaps with tatty rags,
So much rubbish on a split tree
By a dry river bed
Cobbled with flints.

Two flat dead crows,
Wrung out,
White bone, black feathers,
Are dolls of themselves.

Banks open chalk holes,
The stump of an upturned bottle.
The barrow is empty,
Long puddled,
Stone chambers of a stone heart
Choked with mud,
As the day turns, and the year.

# LOVE STORY

## CASSANDRA PHILLIPS-SEARS

I was too young then to understand my parents' faces, why father smashed the lute, called the neighbors, ran the minstrel from the village with night and cold mid-autumn coming on.

I was, though, at the age of learning things by heart, and just old enough to carry tunes without wavering, so I remember still his song, though I have never sung it. Whatever fell between that great doomed lord and his lady it was more than goats' rutting, but I knew even then that it was not for me, nor any here.

The best women here can hope for once their blood has come is nine months in the house and company of a boy as young and scared as we, where we lay abed praying that he and his family will be as kind as they may, praying that the love-songs taught us what we need to know, praying that our womb shall not be barren as an old nut, which they say would bring the dragon on the village.

All this I learned the year my sister was eleven and married John, the baker's son. Five months in I was at last allowed to visit. She had always been fat and rosy-cheeked under her dark hair; peeping from a nest of bed-clothes she looked more like a bird than ever. We spoke of small things, the spring coming soon, her embroidery. She showed it me: a bit to go on the baby's gown come christening-time. It was fine work, delicate and difficult and perfect. It scared me: she had always hated embroidery. And so I, foolish, said the foolish thing I had been thinking of and keeping in those five months: "I remember he used to put flour in your hair when you went for bread. You cannot be happy, Agnes. Do you love him?"

She looked at me and a frown fell between her brows. "What ideas you do have, Mary! Do you think me a side of beef, that this—" she patted her stomach, round as a loaf "—sprang forth from nothing like a grub? There is nothing that I want I do not have."

I knew then that she did not understand me—that no one could—and so left her to her perfect hems.

Five months in she wanted nothing; but seven came soft, and the turning of the year and the new grass-smell blowing in under the door must have wakened something in her, or the child: that day John himself came to our door, haggard under the eyes. "Mary," he said. "Help us." I shook off his hand and waited. "Your Agnes has not slept these three nights past."

Mother came from the house then, pale. "Women want things in their time, boy. What is it? Mary will go and help you."

"Mother!" I thought of his doughy face, his sniveling, the flour in her hair. I know that mother thought of the baby, of the dragon, and as for John, any but a fool could tell his thoughts were only of the sleep he'd get that eve.

His eyes lit. "Thank you, thank you—it is the field-pheasants; all my traps have not caught a one and she says she must have them both or die."

So I spent that day out hunting pheasants; and at the end we brought back and plucked a pair, cock and hen, for her. She ate of them and was finally still.

It is hard work—they are skitterish birds, male and female so unlike each other in feather, color, build, habit, and call that the swallow and the owl are more similar.

It was so hard that I did not notice that my own blood had come 'til I woke from sleep that night. I—knowing, I thought, something of love—determined to hide it as long as I well could. I wanted true-lover's-plaits, whatso'er they were; I wanted something glorious in song and story.

I did very well for nearly six months, enough to see the baby and his godparents, even enough to see a second child start in Agnes and, uncharitably, gleefully, thank God that it was not mine: because I thought I knew of love, I thought no one worthy of mine in either sense, which perhaps was true.

I was also the only one in town thought—could think—tales of dragons come for virgins a fancy, scaring people into making more without the fuss which 'love' would surely cause.

That was not true.

I do not know why the old tales always have such dragons come at night; ours came for me in the late morning as I finished taking stones out the animals' hooves.

There was a great flap of wings, and smell of three-days-rotted meat. It landed in our yard, taking up the space entire: when the rooster, a fey mood on him, went for it, it broke the bird's neck with its sapling tail. My parents stood behind me in the doorway.

It had a voice with a drone, like some great pipe note 'round which spheres shake their stars, or a chuch-bell. "Keep you some maid here from me."

"No," my mother said, or my father.

And then it snuffed the air, and looked at me. "You." Its eyes like hearts of coals.

"No." I started trembling.

Mother knew what I had done, then, and turned back to the house. The smoke my things, blooded or not, made as she burned them reached even up to where the dragon took me. "Your mother is wise. My kin will not now be drawn here," was the beast's only comment.

My father never moved from the doorway as the dragon caged me close round with sun-warmed palms and jumped into the air. I know he wishes now, as I do, that he had beat the song from me.

The dragon sat down on a rock in a high place. It unfurled its hands and I tumbled out, collapsed, on grass halfway between sky and earth.

It prodded me with a talon big as half an ox. I stared at it, crawled up shakily, mouth straight-drawn as embroidery. "If you are going to eat me, eat me."

"I do not eat you. In." It gestured to a hole, a maw, in the cliffside. When I did not move, it picked me up and threw me.

I awoke on a pile of gold coins; dried blood held my hair in twisted elf-locks to my skin. I sat up. My foot kicked something ancient, filigree; it burst in flakes apart, settled into dust.

"Touch nothing!" The dragon blocked the mouth of the cave; treasures reached back into the shadows. It was dawn, or dusk, of the next day; peach rays filtered through the dragon's outstretched wings. Its terrible attention was on me for less than a second before we both heard: the coins, this ancient bloodied cup, this sword, shifting on each other, perhaps?

The unicorn came out from the riches: its hooves, black and dancing, were the ones had tapped the stone, and its grey mane flowed like storm-cloud. Its head whipped snakelike to me, its skin rippled once as wind crosses water. It stood for a moment, pink nostrils stretched smelling wide as any mill-horse's. I called to it, recalling tales of laps and maids and golden collars. Thought myself saved.

The unicorn's overlarge brown eyes, goat-pupilled, unblinking, held the same craving my sister's had. The dragon's words returned: "I do not eat you."

Saw her belly, low and gravid with dragon eggs. Thought of the pheasants.


Certain birds gather about them nests of sticks, bits of shiny rock, and so attract love. Unicorns, it seems, prefer things old, frail, bought with the blood of innocents; this is what dragons collect for them.

I have been three days without food or drink, nor have I had hap to find any; he sits at the entrance and waits.

And maids, the legends of the maids and the unicorns are true: the unicorns chase them about and lay their heads on their laps. Unicorns are very fast; the cave is very small. Their heads, too, are heavy.

Tomorrow I will be too weak to rise.

# GREY DECEMBER

## SHIRL SAZYNSKI

You left me there, in the rain where we first met,
your smile,
first thing that I saw
distinctly in the vague December night.
and your voice so clear against the quiet said:
It's not so gloomy, is it?
It's just the world all hushed up, waiting.
Trying to decide. It
can turn into anything tonight.

And the lights suspended in the fog make me wonder
what the world wants to be tonight
as we lean upon the frosty stone rail
as our words join the grey
as shadows pass us by
silent as moths
floating over London Bridge.

Your lips were red
in the vague December

and so very warm.
It wasn't so gloomy, was it?
It was just the world all hushed up, waiting
for you. Trying to decide
if I was yours
the night.

You left me there
in the rain where we first met
and it's always
always
December.

# BIOGRAPHIES

**Mike Allen** is president of the Science Fiction Poetry Association and editor of the magazine *Mythic Delirium* and the anthology *Mythic*. With Roger Dutcher, Mike is also editor of *The Alchemy of Stars: Rhysling Award Winners Showcase*, which for the first time collects the Rhysling Award-winning poems from 1978 to 2004 in one volume. His newest poetry collections, *Disturbing Muses* and *Strange Wisdoms of the Dead*, are both available from Wildside Press. He lives in Roanoke, VA, with his wife Anita, two comical dogs and a demonic cat.

**Veronica Schanoes** is a writer and scholar with a particular interest in myths and fairy tales. Her work has appeared in *Lady Churchill's Rosebud Wristlet* and has won the William Carlos Williams Prize from the Academy of American Poets. Raised in New York City, she has been working on her English Ph.D. at the University of Pennsylvania, and is currently living in London.

Shy and nocturnal, **Jennifer Crow** has never been photographed in the wild. She lives in a little house made of books, and recites poetry on her porch when the moon is full. If you want to catch up with her work, you can find it in recent issues of *Illumen, Star\*Line*, and *Mythic Delirium*, as well as online at *Strange Horizons* and *Abyss & Apex*.

**Megan Messinger**, a San Francisco native transplanted to New York, has published (mostly) prose and (some) poetry in a range of print magazines and webzines, most recently *Aoife's Kiss, Vestal Review*, and *Fantasy Magazine*. She is currently in hot pursuit of a B.A. in English from Barnard College.

**Ann K. Schwader** lives and writes in Westminster, CO. Her work has recently appeared in *Dreams & Nightmares, Iambs & Trochees, Mythic Delirium,* and elsewhere. See more of her work on her website: **www.geocities.com/hpl4ever/**.

**Catherynne M. Valente** writes novels and poetry and occasionally deconstructs Greek plays for fun and profit. Her novels include *The Labyrinth, Yume no Hon: TheBook of Dreams, The Grass-Cutting Sword* and, forthcoming in November, *The Orphan's Tales*. Her poetry books include *Apocrypha* and *Oracles*.

**Tim Pratt**'s poems have appeared in *Asimov's, Strange Horizons*, and other nice places, and his first poetry collection, *If There Were Wolves*, is coming out in mid-2006. He won the

Rhysling for best long poem in 2005, and he lives in Oakland with his wife, Heather Shaw.

**Constance Cooper** has worked as a journalist, balloon animal twister, linguistic researcher and software engineer. She has sold work to *Asimov's Science Fiction, Abyss & Apex, Mythic Delirium, Black Gate*, and *Andromeda Spaceways Inflight Magazine*. Find out more about her writing at **constance.bierner.org**.

**Jeannelle M. Ferreirra** is twice twelve years old, has been writing since she was six, and holds a degree in Creative Writing from Brandeis University. She enjoys listening to stories and swimming off the coast of Massachusetts; she divides her time between her family's farm there and Washington, D.C. *A Verse From Babylon* is her first published novel.

**Sonya Taaffe** has a confirmed addiction to folklore, mythology, dead languages, and all possible combinations of the above. Her poem "Matlacihuatl's Gift" shared first place for the 2003 Rhysling Award, and a respectable amount of her work has been collected in *Singing Innocence and Experience* and *Postcards from the Province of Hyphens*. She is currently pursuing a Ph.D. in Classics at Yale University, and has difficulty talking about herself in the third person. "Countries of the Sun" was created around the seventh-century Standard Version of the Epic of Gilgamesh; its seven component poems each take their name from some line in the text. Those curious about the Babylonian epic are encouraged to check out Benjamin Foster's translation (Norton Critical Editions, 2001) and Andrew George's comprehensive transliteration, translation, and commentary (Oxford University Press, 2003). "Countries of the Sun" is dedicated to Eckart Frahm, whose fault it is that I decided to learn Akkadian, and to Torger Vedeler, whose fault it is that I know how.

**Rio Le Moignan** is from Guernsey, gets on better with her siblings than seems completely normal, and does care work to support her writing habit. Her only previously published poem is online at *Strange Horizons*, and she welcomes visitors to her journal at **www.livejournal/users/apotropaism**

A University of Pennsylvania graduate, **Sarah Koplik** is currently pursuing a PhD in Near Eastern Studies at The Johns Hopkins University. In the summers she can be found happily playing in the dirt at one of the many archaeological sites in the Middle East. She is an avid reader of ancient history, mythology, and all types of science fiction and fantasy.

**JoSelle Vanderhooft** is a Utah-based poet, novelist and free-lance writer. Her books include *10,000 Several Doors, The Tale* of the Miller's Daughter, Vice of Kings, Enter, Elsinore and Desert Songs among others. Her poetry and short stories have appeared or will appear online and in print in Star*Line, Cabinet des Fées, Sybil's Garage, MythicDelirium, The Seventh Quarry and others.

**Laurel Winter** grew up in the mountains of Montana and attended a one-room country grade school with twelve to twenty-five students in grades 1 through 8. She then went thirty miles one way on the bus to Absarokee High School, where there were thirty-three in her graduating class. Since then she's acquired an eclectic education, including credits in English, physics, and psychology from Montana State and numerous writing and art classes. She is currently studying energy medicine.

Her first novel, *Growing Wings*, was a finalist for the Mythopoeic Award for children's fantasy and she's won back-to-back Rhysling and Asimov's Readers' Poll Awards for best poem, a World Fantasy Award for best Novella ("Sky Eyes"), and the 2003 McKnight Artist Fellowship for children's fiction.

She has twin sons who have graduated from high school. Laurel belongs to a thirteen-pound black cat named Panther.

**Holly Phillips** is the author of the critically acclaimed collection of literary fantasy stories *In the Palace of Repose* and *The Burning Girl*, her first novel. She has lived in southeastern British Columbia, Canada, for most of her life, and wouldn't really want to live anywhere else, despite the occasional frustrations of living in a small town. She does love to travel when she gets the chance.

**Ainsley Dicks** has long had a tumultuous but rewarding relationship with literature, mythology, and folklore, and her poetry and prose have previously been published in *Culture Shock* and the *Queen's Feminist Review*. A Newfoundlander born and raised, Ainsley currently resides in Connecticut with her soulmate, Andrew, whilst pursuing a Ph.D. in Assyriology at Yale University.

A sophomore at Barnard College, **Jaida Jones** won a Scholastic Writing Portfolio Award in 2004, subsequently edited *The Best Teen Writing: 2005*, and recently appeared in *Mythic Delirium*.

**Yoon Ha Lee's** poetry has previously appeared in *Star\*Line* and *The Magazine of Speculative Poetry*. She uses her husband, an astrophysics doctoral candidate, shamelessly as a resource, and thinks everyone should have a pet physicist. You can see more of her work on her website, **pegasus.cityofveils.com**, or send her email at **requiescat@cityofveils.com**.

**Richard Parks** lives in Mississippi, which arguably produces more writers per capita than anywhere else in the country. Whether this is something in the water or simply for the want of something better to do is an open question. His stories have appeared in *Asimov's SF, Realms of Fantasy, SF Age, Amazing Stories*, *Weird Tales*, and *Lady Churchill's Rosebud Wristlet*, among other places. PS Publishing will bring out his novella, *Hereafter and After*, as a signed limited edition in late 2006. His second collection, *Worshipping Small Gods*, is due out from Prime Books in June 2006.

**Theodora Goss** has been writing poetry since she can remember. Her poems have been published in magazines such as *Mythic Delirium* and *The Lyric*, and reprinted in *The Year's Best Fantasy and Horror*. She recently won a Rhysling Award. Her chapbook of short stories and poems, *The Rose in Twelve Petals & Other Stories*, was published by Small Beer Press, and a short story collection, *In the Forest of Forgetting*, is currently forthcoming. She lives in Boston, where she is completing a PhD in English literature, with her husband, daughter, and cats. Her website address is **www.theodoragoss.com**.

**Jane Yolen**, whose stories are loved by children and adults all around the world, is the author of over two hundred books, including novels, picture books, story collections, poetry, and nonfiction—leading *Publishers Weekly* to call her "America's own Hans Christian Andersen." Her many magical books include *Briar Rose, Sister Light, Sister Dark, White Jenna, The One-Armed Queen* (for adults); *and Owl Moon, The Faery Flag, Dream Weaver, Neptune Rising, The Devil's Arithmetic*, and the Young Merlin series (for children). Her books have won the Caldecott Medal, the Regina Medal, the Kerlan Award, the Society of Children's Book Writers Award, the Mythopoeic Award, the Daedalus Award, the Christopher Medal, and numerous other honors.

Jane divides her time between homes in western Massachusetts and St. Andrews, Scotland.

**Erzebet YellowBoy**'s short stories have appeared in *Fantasy Magazine* and are forthcoming in *Not One of Us* and *Sleeping Beauty, Indeed*. She is the founder of Papaveria Press and co-editor of *Cabinet des Fées*, a journal of fairy tale fiction and in her spare time, she plays with bones.

**Helena Bell** (or **Hel**) lives in Carbondale, Illinois, where she is pursing an MFA in Poetry from Southern Illinois University. Her poetry has appeared in *Strange Horizons, Strong Verse*, and her grandmother's refrigerator.

**Elizabeth Wein**'s young adult novels include *The Winter Prince, A Coalition of Lions* and *The Sunbird*, all set in Arthurian Britain and sixth century Ethiopia. The cycle continues in *The Lion*

*Hunter* and *The Mark of Solomon* (Viking 2006). Elizabeth has short stories forthcoming in Datlow and Windling's *The Coyote Road* anthology and the "Reckless" issue of Michael Cart's *Rush Hour* (Spring 2006). Elizabeth has a PhD in Folklore from the University of Pennsylvania. She lives in Scotland with her husband and two small children, and frequently squanders writing time keeping her pilot's license current. Her web site is **www.elizabethwein.com.**

**Sarah Singleton** was born in rural Northamptonshire and holds an honours degree in English Literature and Language from the University of Nottingham. She travelled in Europe, India and Nepal, and worked variously with horses, in a chocolate shop, as a factory operative, and a chambermaid in Germany, before becoming a journalist.

In 1993 she married Brian Hoare, and they have two young daughters. Now, she lives in Chippenham, "in beautiful mystic Wiltshire," and works as a senior reporter for the *Wiltshire Gazette & Herald*, campaigns with a local human rights group, and is learning to play violin.

She is the author of *The Crow Maiden*, *Century*, and *Heretic*.

**Cassandra Phillips-Sears** lives in Cambridge, Massachusetts; she has a plum pudding mold and knows how to use it.

**Shirl Sazynski** believes in the pursuit of knowledge and all things beautiful—and an insoucient perception of gender, exploring the history of the beautiful male embraced in Japanese pop culture (**www.bishoneninfo.com**). A student at Hollins University, she is a regular contributor to *Animerica* magazine, editorial assistant at *Mythic Delirium*—and simultaneously attempting to learn ancient Greek, martial arts and how to play the harp—though not necessarily at the same time.

*coetus audire silentum,*
*nosse domos Stygias arcanaque Ditis operti*
*non superi, non uita uetat.*

To listen in at the couplings of the silent,
to know the homes of the Styx and the secrets of opened Dis,
not the gods, not life forbid her.

—Lucan, *Civil War.*